Penguin Books

What is to be done abou...

Jeannette Mitchell was born and grew up in West Yorkshire. She was educated at Sussex University, where she gained a degree in developmental psychology. In 1973 she went to work as Assistant Director of the Community Development Project Information and Intelligence Unit, whose task was to co-ordinate the joint work of the twelve Home Office community development projects in declining inner-city areas. At the unit Jeannette Mitchell was involved in writing and publishing a series of reports which were critical of government policy towards the inner city. After the project was closed down in November 1976 she was taken on by the Social Evaluation Unit at Oxford University to continue the publishing work.

Following a period of unemployment Jeannette Mitchell worked as Secretary to Brent Community Health Council from November 1977 until June 1981. In October 1981 she was recruited by *The Times* to work as a journalist on its new Health Supplement, and when it folded she joined *The Times* newspaper until July 1982 where she primarily covered the 1982 health workers' industrial action. She now works for the Greater London Council, specializing in health policy. She is a co-author of *In and Against the State* (1980).

Jeannette Mitchell is a member of the Politics of Health Group, who have supported her in writing *What is to be done about illness and health?*. POHG is an open discussion group of socialist and feminist health workers and others with a special interest in health politics. It can be contacted at 9 Poland Street, London W1.

The series in which this book appears is sponsored by the Socialist Society, a broad-based, independent organization devoted to furthering socialist research, debate and education. Membership of the Society is open to all individuals and organizations who support its principles and objectives. Details of these, and other information about the work of the Society, may be obtained from: The Socialist Society, 9 Poland Street, London W1.

WHAT IS TO BE DONE ABOUT ILLNESS AND HEALTH?

Jeannette Mitchell

Penguin Books

Penguin Books Ltd, Harmondsworth, Middlesex, England
Penguin Books, 40 West 23rd Street, New York, New York 10010, U.S.A.
Penguin Books Australia Ltd, Ringwood, Victoria, Australia
Penguin Books Canada Ltd, 2801 John Street, Markham, Ontario, Canada L3R 1B4
Penguin Books (N.Z.) Ltd, 182–190 Wairau Road, Auckland 10, New Zealand

First published 1984

Made and printed in Great Britain by
Cox & Wyman Ltd, Reading
Filmset in 10/12 pt Monophoto Ehrhardt by
Northumberland Press Ltd, Gateshead

Contents

A Worker's Speech to a Doctor

We know what makes us ill.
When we are ill we are told
That it is you who will heal us.

For ten years, we are told,
You learned healing in fine schools
Built at the people's expense
And to get your knowledge
Spent a fortune.
So you must be able to heal.

Are you able to heal?
When we come to you
Our rags are torn off us
And you listen all over our naked body.
As to the cause of our illness
One glance at our rags would
Tell you more. It is the same cause that wears out
Our bodies and our clothes.

The pain in our shoulder comes,
You say, from the damp; and this is also the reason
For the stain on the wall of our flat.
So tell us:
Where does the damp come from?

Too much work and too little food
Makes us feeble and thin.

Your prescription says:
Put on more weight
You might as well tell a bullrush
Not to get wet.

How much time can you give us?
We see: one carpet in your flat costs
The fees you earn from five thousand consultations.

You'll no doubt say
You are innocent. The damp patch
On the wall of our flats
Tells the same story.

BERTOLT BRECHT

Acknowledgements

This book is a personal statement of what I have learned through being part of the Politics of Health Group. Like earlier writing by members of the group (particularly Lesley Doyal's *The Political Economy of Health*[1] and Mick Carpenter's 'Left Orthodoxy and the Politics of Health'[2]), it has been written with the advice, support and criticism of members of the group. Throughout the period of writing Nancy Worcester and Gene Feder have been my support group, reading drafts and re-drafts, pressing always for clarification of ideas and for moderation in their presentation. Combating writers' defensiveness is a thankless task. It is a reflection of Nancy and Gene's determination and commitment that they stuck with me. Many other members of the group have helped along the way, too, reading specific bits and coming to discussions of the ideas, among them Claire Chatelet, Duncan Keeley, Paul McKeague, Diane Pampling, Jane Salvage, Paul O'Brien, Hilary Prentice, Carol Smith, Mike Joffe, Lesley Doyal, Aubrey Sheiham, Patrick Byrne, Maggie Eisner, Jos Cornwall, Sarah Martin, Jill Yudkin, John Yudkin and Tony Fletcher.

Michael Marmot, Alex Scott-Samuel, Alison Macfarlane and Jean Robinson also kindly read drafts. In preparing the epidemiological evidence I was helped by Dave Leon, David Jones and Kath Moser, who work at the City University, London, on the *Longitudinal Study*, and David Albury of the North East London Polytechnic. Sue Kingswell of the Coventry Workshop and Christine Green of Darnall Road Surgery, Sheffield, helped with arranging the interviews. Shan Jagedo, Les Bennett, Andrew Tree, Ruth Hutchinson, Baden Gough, Ethel Fraser,

George Taylor and Vera Mitchell gave their time not only to be interviewed but to read drafts and make changes to them. I am grateful to them and to my sister, Caroline Mitchell, for their time, their work, their frankness and their willingness to share personal and sometimes distressing experiences.

Much of the experience on which the book is based comes from the time when I worked at Brent Community Health Council. At the CHC I worked first with Sally Goldsmith and later with Marianne Craig. The perspectives of the book come out of our work and two very special friendships.

Preface

The purpose of this book is to sketch how medicine and health care might be different. It sets out some of the issues to be explored in thinking about the health care we need.

It aims to be positive, to make a statement that things do not have to be as they are now. Being constructive, however, involves deconstructing some myths: myths about what medicine can and can't do; myths about the origin and nature of illness and disease. You will find that some parts of this book are very angry. It is an anger which comes from having shared many, many people's painful experiences of the health service. It is an anger about what stands between us and better health.

Doctors may feel under fire. Particularly if they themselves are battling for change within the health service, they may feel they are the subject of unjust criticism. I hope, however, that they will bear their discomfort, recognizing that unless the present dissatisfaction with medicine is plainly stated, nothing will change. For my part, I recognize that although to outsiders the National Health Service may seem like a monolith, there are arguments and discussions going on within it all the time about how health care could be better. In writing this book one of the intentions is to strengthen the hand of those health workers – including doctors – who are trying to develop a different kind of practice.

Our arguments draw primarily on English evidence and experience. This is because what we have to say about the role of health care is in some ways specific to the National Health Service. A longer and more detailed book would have looked at the issues from an international perspective. The patterns of health and illness in other industrialized countries, including the

Eastern bloc, are similar to those in Britain. In the under-developed and newly industrializing countries there are different patterns of mortality and morbidity, but these nevertheless reflect the same worldwide social forces which bear on us in Britain. Our arguments about health care in Britain also apply in many ways to Western medicine as it is practised in most parts of the world. In China there have been important attempts to transform medical practice, but in Russia and Eastern Europe, while there have been encouraging innovations in the organization of health care, the medicine practised differs little from that we know in the West.

In developing our argument I make use both of research and of experience. Part Two, which develops a critique of the health service, draws particularly on what I have learned through personal encounters with patients, doctors, administrators, civil servants, ancillary workers, nurses and paramedical staff. In many places I have found that the clearest way of explaining what I mean has been to give very specific examples. You will find no names, places, times or dates, however; I have chosen to write about people's experiences in a way which abstracts them from the specific circumstances in which I learned of them. This is partly to ensure the anonymity of those involved and partly because they are not meant to be horror stories but to act as a concrete reflection of general experience.

Introduction

In the High Street there are three furniture shops. Behind one window, a cardboard notice propped on the arm of a settee offers easy terms: buy now, pay later. During shopping hours, kitchen chairs and coffee tables spill out on to the street, secured by thin metal chains. Among these pavement bargains there are always two or three folding beds. Some have thin mattresses only an inch or two wide. The ones with thick mattresses have wood-grain formica shelves across the top.

People buy the fold-up beds because where they live there is not enough space for everyone to have their own proper bed. Each year the council housing waiting list gets longer. At the moment, to get a flat you need more than a hundred points. A woman, a man and two children living in two rooms may qualify after five years. Those in better conditions must wait a lifetime, living meanwhile with other members of the family or in private rented rooms. The landlords charge around £20 a week for two rooms, one with a sink and a stove in it, and the use of a shared bathroom and toilet.

After years of campaigning, some of the terraced houses once owned by the private landlords have been bought up by the council. For the same rent you get more space and your own kitchen and bathroom. But often the conversions have been done on the cheap. The council is slow to carry out repairs on leaking roofs and fallen ceilings.

Beyond the terraced streets, over a mile from the shops, are the big estates. The biggest, a maze of interlocking giant blocks in barren yellow earth, was first planned in the early 1960s. The scheme looked so grim that the councillors threw it out. Four years later, in the face of growing waiting lists and dwindling resources, it was revived. Now it has become a place where only the most desperate live. Anxiety is a way of life. The old and chronically ill worry about being stranded when the lifts break down. There is always the fear that young children playing indoors will fall from the windows. They cannot play outside unless you go with them. In the anonymous open spaces, long corridors and empty car parks, there is no one to witness attacks on women, black people and the elderly.

Another estate of shining white concrete has just been completed. The flats have been designed with all-electric heating. The bills are much more than most tenants can afford. The tenants' association has won a rebate from the council, but still older people will not use the heating. In the winter they go to the library during the day, and in the evenings they sit in their coats by single-bar electric fires. Many younger people are in debt. Those who have had the electricity disconnected cook by candle light on camping stoves loaned by the social services. The children are cold. Sometimes there are fires.

Squeezed among the shops, houses and council offices, there are small factories and works employing between ten and fifty people. You can find a job paying £45 for a forty-hour week. If you do not work at the required rate the supervisor docks your pay. The pace drains your strength. Eight hours a day of chemical fumes and splinters of metal in your fingers. There is one toilet. Sometimes even if you are pregnant they keep you waiting before you are allowed to go. You eat your lunch at the bench. Forming a union is a long and bitter struggle.

There are better-paid jobs, though they are harder to get, in the factories on the vast industrial estate which stretches from the railway line to the horizon. At night familiar names of biscuits, bread, soft drinks and household products glow in neon from the serrated roofs. People in unskilled jobs take home £60. Working shifts enables you to fit in with the children, but there is precious little leisure-time left. The unions struggle to hold off management plans to cut jobs and speed up the work. The managers have said that unless the workers agree to productivity improvements and rationalization schemes, they will close the factory and invest their capital elsewhere.

Every year more of the factories on the estate shut down. Now that most of the engineering works have closed, there are few skilled jobs. Some factories have been replaced by warehouses, offering a few places to school-leavers. A new hypermarket is being built. Men with dogs guard the empty sites.

Here, beyond the shops, beyond the houses and the tower blocks, among the factories, warehouses and derelict sites, is the hospital. Once an old workhouse amid green fields backing on to the canal, it has become the main hospital in the district. Despite its distance from where people live, it has been favoured by the authorities for expansion over the decades because of the surrounding abundance of cheap land for new building. With other hospitals closing, it is now the only one serving not just this area, but three or four more suburbs even further away. Local people call the hospital by the same name as the industrial estate, but the health authorities call it the Central Hospital.

A baby dies. The distraught mother is convinced it was a needless death. Worried by her child's illness she had taken her, with her twin sister and her older sister, to Casualty the previous evening. To get to the hospital from where she lives, you have to take two buses. During the daytime you can wait more than half an hour. In the rush hour the buses are often so full that three or four go past before you can get on. At the hospital, after the child had been examined the woman was told to bring her back next morning. The next day, unable to face the long journey with the three children, one of them now very sick, she did not go back. In the afternoon the child died. The doctors and the hospital administrators blame the woman. How irresponsible to disobey the hospital's instructions, they scream.

Among the workplaces on the industrial estate, the hospital is one of the biggest employers. Over a thousand people work there.

Many of the nurses, porters, cleaners, lab technicians, clerks, kitchen and laundry staff live locally on the estates or in the streets beyond the High Street. If you are a domestic or a nursing auxiliary the average take-home pay for a forty-hour week is around £50. A porter can sometimes make another £20 or £30 working long hours, evenings and weekends.

In their dealings with the workers, the hospital managers, administrators, personnel officers and domestic supervisors use the same management principles on which the factories all around are run. For the hospital managers, like the factory managers, what matters is rationalization and productivity, getting fewer workers to do more. The staff complain they are losing their contact with their patients. The work is more intense, routine and tiring.

In the hospital the patients as well as the workers are the subjects of the industrial management system. The patients are the product. Hospital managers measure efficiency by measuring throughput. They aspire to get the maximum number of patients through the minimum number of beds in the shortest possible time. Hospitals with low throughput risk closure. For the purposes of measuring efficiency, deaths and discharges are categorized together.

The authorities do not attempt to assess whether, between input and output, people get better or worse, grow weaker or stronger, feel served or abused. This is a subjective matter, we are told, not suitable for objective evaluation. But the statistics do give us some clues: the hospital is busy; the people are not well. In fact the hospital is so busy that once a month or so it has to close its doors. All except the most dire emergencies must go elsewhere; doctors and administrators feel under pressure to send their least sick patients home.

And the statistics also tell us that among those who live in the flats and on the estates, who shop in the High Street, fight for the buses, work on the railway, in the factories and in the hospital, more babies are born dead, more children are handicapped, more adults die younger, there is more chronic illness, heart trouble and a hundred other illnesses, than among those who live in the green suburbs and have well-paid jobs.

To the hospital people bring all the accumulated pain and strain of the destructive and hostile environment: accidents; ulcers; bowel and lung cancer; heart attacks; asthma; bronchitis; TB; anxiety; depression; loneliness.

The doctors, preoccupied by coping with high workloads and dwindling resources, devote their spare energy to refining their treatments. To each other and in professional journals they admit they have no cures for most of the medical problems which confront them every day. Why some people rather than others get ill has never been a primary interest of most doctors, but from time to time, in teaching students and in learned gatherings, the high incidence of many illnesses among the lower social classes is noted. Explaining to a colleague, they confide 'Of course, in an area like this . . .' But in all the conversations the assumption is that the people are the problem. Those who used to be called the feckless and are now in more progressive circles referred to as the deprived have unhealthy life-styles. Stubborn, ineducable, self-indulgent, thinking only of today and never of tomorrow, the feckless destroy their own health.

On the wards and in the consulting rooms those who fall outside the doctors' own consensual world – women, black people, people without professional jobs, the elderly, the un-employed – receive the theory made practice: Why did you let your husband put a knife up your vagina? You should have been on the pill. You should come off the pill. Stop smoking. You're over-eating. You should change your job, your house, your boyfriend . . .

And so we are returned faster, but rarely fundamentally healthier, to the cramped houses, the exhausting jobs, the lone-liness of the silent estates, the worry of debt and of more ill health.

On the one hand we have a society in which those who have

the least power suffer the worst health. On the other there is a medical system, itself a microcosm of that society, which takes people from it and returns them to it.

This book is about the relationship between the society which steals our health and the medical system, a system which is a part of, and yet appears apart from, the network of relationships and social processes which lands us in its hands. We shall be asking: Where do the chronic illnesses, heart attacks, cancers and handicaps come from? Why do some people get them and others not? Is all this illness inevitable? What is the medical system doing to remedy the problems we face? Could medicine and health care be different?

Part One

What Ails Us?

1 Who Gets Ill?

When one individual inflicts bodily injury upon another, such injury that death results, we call the deed manslaughter; when the assailant knew in advance the injury would be fatal, we call this deed murder. But when society places hundreds of proletarians in such a position that they inevitably meet a too early and unnatural death . . . and yet permits these conditions to remain, its deed is just as surely murder as the deed of the single individual.

Friedrich Engels[1]

There are two myths about illness. The first is that it usually strikes at random, without apparent rhyme or reason. Illness, we are led to believe, is a matter of fate; it comes out of the blue. The second myth is that these days illnesses are diseases of affluence. We have a hazy notion that once upon a time, maybe in Victorian times, illness had something to do with social conditions. We remember hearing about rickets and T B. But we rarely think of today's complaints, like back pain, ulcers, cancer or heart disease, in the same way.

Heart disease is the most common cause of death among men in their middle years. In 1969 researchers from the London School of Hygiene and Tropical Medicine began recording the deaths from heart disease among men who worked in the civil service in Whitehall.[2] In the following seven years over a thousand died, almost half from heart attacks. Among the 960 civil servants on the top grades there were only nine deaths. Among the 1,625 men on the bottom grades, eighty-seven died. Among the senior civil servants the death rate was less than one in a hundred. Among the messengers and other men doing unskilled work on the bottom grades it was more than one in twenty.

The men on the lowest grades were on average slightly older than the top men, but even after the age difference had been taken into account the men on the bottom grades were almost four times more likely to die than the top civil servants. The death rates for the men on intermediate grades followed the same pattern. The men on clerical grades, the book-keepers and computer operators, had a death rate three times greater than the men on the top grades, and even the men on professional and executive grades had twice the death rate of the top civil servants.

The myths are in question. Our health is as intimately linked with the conditions of our lives as it was a century ago. As for diseases of affluence, there is clearly something wrong with the idea that heart attacks are an 'executive's condition'.

It's official

The study on civil servants was exceptional in that it compared four clearly defined groups of people. Much of what else we know about the relation between class and health comes from official nationwide government statistics. The categories used for analysing information about illness and death tend to be broad and diffuse. Most of what we know is based on the Registrar-General's six social classes, which means that people with quite different incomes and life-styles – the small shopkeeper and the managing director of a multinational company, for instance – can get grouped together.[3] Official statistics also tell us more about men than women. The categories of analysis for married women are based on the husband's occupation, so how a woman's own life affects her health becomes invisible. Even where the categorization is based on the woman's own job, as with single women, the information we get is frustrating, because women's lives cannot be summed up by their jobs, particularly when they have children.[4]

But though official statistics may underestimate the extent of class differences and obscure the factors bearing on women's health, they are nevertheless revealing, confirming the pattern of the civil servants' deaths. Government statistics show that a class pattern of illness and death is to be found among the majority of common illnesses, applying to women as well as men, and bearing on us from before we are born until long into retirement.

The most recent figures for class differences in adult health come from the Registrar-General's *Decennial Supplement* on occupational mortality, which looks at death rates in the period 1970 to 1972.[5] They show that women and men in social class five, the category for people in unskilled jobs, are two and a half times more likely to die before they reach retirement than the professional people who make up social class one. Even when adjustment is made for age, the death rate of people at the bottom of society is still twice that of people at the top.[6] The Office of Population Censuses and Surveys estimates that on average a man born into social class one will live seven years longer than a man born into social class five.[7]

Most mortality statistics categorize men by the jobs they do. If you are a hospital ancillary worker you are twice as likely to be dead before you retire than if you're a senior administrator. Twice as many miners as coal board officials die before they are sixty-five. The university lecturer is three times more likely to live to enjoy his retirement than the machine tool operator. Yet what the statistics also tell us is that while our health is clearly linked to the jobs we do, it is not just the jobs in themselves that affect us. The difference in life expectancy between the miner's wife and the coal board official's wife is even greater than their husbands'; the miner's wife faces two and a half times the risk of untimely death. The death rate of women married to teachers or social workers is half that of fishermen's wives and a third of that of building labourers' wives.[8]

Looking at indicators other than jobs reveals the same pattern. The government's ongoing *Longitudinal Study*, which is examining mortality rates in relation to information from the census, has shown that if you have two cars and live in an owner-occupied

(a)

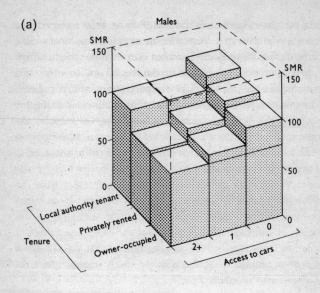

(b)

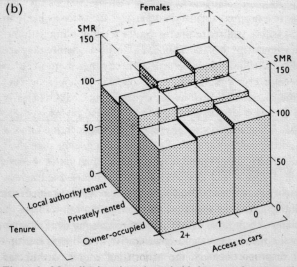

Figure 1. Mortality in private households by type of tenure and access to cars, by cause of death. Source: OPCS *Longitudinal Study*.

house you have almost half the risk of dying before you retire of someone who lives in a council house and does not have a car.[9]

The quality of our health cannot of course be judged simply by how long we live. Our everyday health matters too. The *General Household Survey*, a yearly government study, indicates that working-class people also suffer chronic illnesses disproportionately.[10] Since 1972 the survey has consistently found that people in social class five report twice the level of 'limiting long-standing sickness'. Short-term illnesses such as flu, however, do not appear to be so closely linked with class.

Table 1 *Everyday health problems*

	% ill in previous fortnight	% reporting long-standing illness	% reporting limiting long-standing illness
Social class I:			
Men	12	22	12
Women	16	26	13
Social class V:			
Men	13	36	24
Women	14	41	28

Source: *General Household Survey 1980* (HMSO, 1982).

The social pyramid

Inequality in illness and death is often seen as the problem of a small group on the margins of society. We tend to think of the population being fairly evenly distributed among the Registrar-General's social classes and imagine that even if some people suffer disproportionately, the majority of us are not affected. Dominant thinking in social policy circles focuses on the plight

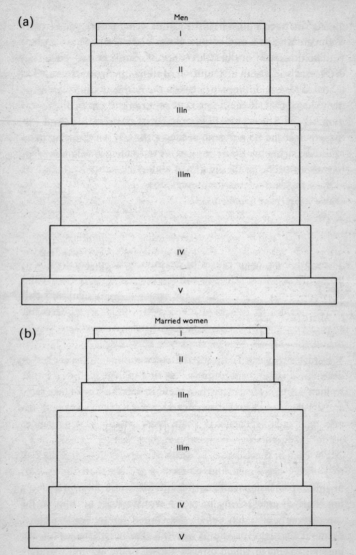

Figure 2. The social pyramid of death. Deaths from all causes by social class: the length of each bar corresponds to the death rate; the width of the bar corresponds to the number of people in each social group.

of 'the deprived'. So we tend to think of unnecessary ill health as the problem of a small group of unfortunate people. But when you look carefully at the relative size of the Registrar-General's categories and at the distribution of illness between them, what is striking is the difference between the health of the majority of people and that of the 5 per cent or so at the top of the social pyramid. The death rate of men in social class one is a third less than that of the 65 per cent of men classified as having manual jobs. Among women the class gap is even wider. Women married to men in professional jobs have almost half the death rate of women married to men in manual jobs.

The big killers

There are four major causes of death in modern Britain: circulatory diseases (heart disease and strokes), cancer, accidents, and chest diseases. Accidents are the major killer of children and young people. In the middle years, cancer, heart disease and strokes account for four out of five deaths. In later years most people die of heart attacks, strokes or chest diseases.

Figure 3 (overleaf) shows the distribution of the causes of death in different age groups. At first glance it appears that women suffer more cancer than men. In fact their mortality rates are similar; it is just that women in general have a lower death rate than men, particularly from heart attacks, and so cancer accounts for a greater proportion of their deaths.

For each of these causes of death at every stage of life the risk to working-class men and women is greater than the risk to people in professional and managerial jobs. The class differences for heart disease among men are smaller than for any major category of death for either sex. When contrasted with the dramatic findings of the Whitehall study this points to the possible extent to which official statistics may generally underestimate class differences.[11] It is also worth noting that in the

(a)

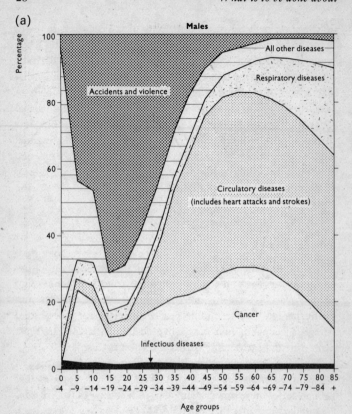

Figure 3. Selected causes of death: by age and sex, 1979. Source: Office of Population Censuses and Surveys; General Register Office (Scotland); General Register Office (Northern Ireland).

official statistics there is a far sharper class difference among women than among men. The pattern for respiratory diseases and accidents is even more dramatic. Paradoxically the category of accidents which shows the sharpest class differences is deaths to pedestrians. It is not the people that own the cars who die from them.

(b)

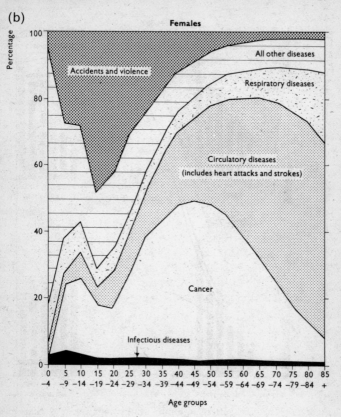

Cancer accounts for nearly half the deaths among women in middle years and a quarter of the deaths of men in this age group. One in four people now gets cancer. Different kinds of cancer have different class patterns. Leukaemia, for instance, appears to have no clear link with class, and breast cancer is peculiar in occurring *less* often among working-class women. But for most other forms of cancer the link with class is frightening. Lung cancer and stomach cancer, two of the most common forms,

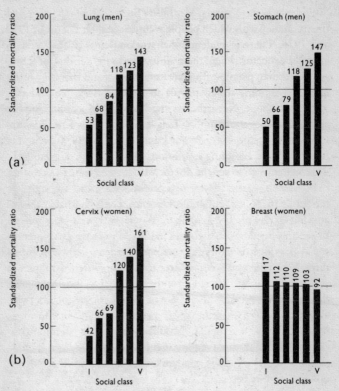

Figure 4. The class pattern of cancer deaths: four key sites. Source: *Occupational Mortality 1970–1972* (HMSO, 1978), pp. 48–9, and microfiche tables.

occur twice as often among men in manual jobs as among men in professional jobs. Four times as many women die of cervical cancer in social class five as in social class one.

Common complaints

We know much less about who gets common everyday illnesses like back pain, bronchitis or digestive problems. The main source of evidence is the National Morbidity Survey,[12] which examined the frequency with which people went to see their doctor in 1970 and 1971. There is evidence that working-class people tend to go to the doctor when their illness is more serious or more advanced than people with professional jobs, and that they often ignore symptoms which people in social classes one and two would see about. Nevertheless the National Morbidity Survey reveals a clear pattern among long-term and recurrent illnesses. Chronic bronchitis is a major cause of time off work and a persistent and disabling condition. Women with husbands in unskilled jobs go to see the doctor with it three times more often than women married to men in professional jobs. Among their husbands there is a four-fold difference. With bad backs, bones and joints, the picture is similar. Women in social class one go to see the doctor with arthritis half as frequently as women in social class five. Doctors see men in unskilled jobs with slipped discs, back pain and sciatica three times more often than men in professional jobs. Ulcers, another so-called 'businessman's disease', drive men at the bottom of society to the doctors twice as frequently as men at the top. Top men die of ulcers four times less frequently than men in unskilled jobs. Other common conditions for which there is the same kind of class pattern include varicose veins, phlebitis, anaemia, chronic digestive problems, epilepsy and diabetes.

For what doctors categorize as 'mental disorders' the most striking difference is between men and women rather than between classes. On average, women go to see the doctor about what are diagnosed as psychiatric problems twice as often as men. Among women there is a class pattern for the diagnoses of psychosis, insomnia, tension headache and 'unclassifiable symptoms'; but, for all of these conditions, even women in social class one visit the doctor twice as often as men in general. Among people diagnosed as having depression, the pattern again reflects both sex and class. Women have far higher rates than men, but, significantly, married women suffer worse than single women.

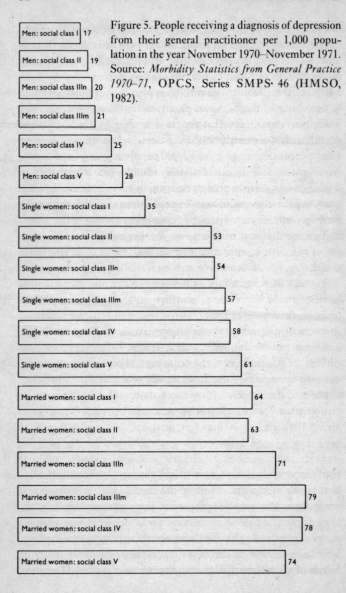

Figure 5. People receiving a diagnosis of depression from their general practitioner per 1,000 population in the year November 1970–November 1971. Source: *Morbidity Statistics from General Practice 1970–71*, OPCS, Series SMPS· 46 (HMSO, 1982).

Men: social class I 17

Men: social class II 19

Men: social class IIIn 20

Men: social class IIIm 21

Men: social class IV 25

Men: social class V 28

Single women: social class I 35

Single women: social class II 53

Single women: social class IIIn 54

Single women: social class IIIm 57

Single women: social class IV 58

Single women: social class V 61

Married women: social class I 64

Married women: social class II 63

Married women: social class IIIn 71

Married women: social class IIIm 79

Married women: social class IV 78

Married women: social class V 74

Among all three groups, people in social class one suffer least.

Beyond what is known about who goes to the doctor, there is little research which indicates the true extent of our everyday health problems. Two important studies, however, show how much suffering among working-class people does not even come to the notice of their general practitioners. The National Morbidity Survey indicates that people in professional jobs go to the doctor with worries about their hearing more frequently than other people. But a survey of 12,000 people in Glasgow, Cardiff, Nottingham and Southampton[13] found that slightly more working-class people possess hearing aids, indicating that the hearing problems middle-class people go to the doctor with are generally less severe. When the researchers measured the extent of people's hearing problems in the general population they found twice the level of disabling deafness among working-class people.

A study of women in Camberwell interviewed in their own homes[14] found that twice as many women were experiencing the problems and feelings a psychiatrist would label 'clinical depression' than were going to the doctor about it. Six per cent of women categorized as middle-class were found to have had acute clinical depression in the preceding three months. Among working-class women the figure was 23 per cent. The prevalence of chronic depression lasting more than a year was five times greater among working-class women.

From birth to death

Our present conditions also affect the new generation. Malformations of the brain and spinal cord occur in the first few weeks after conception, even before the pregnancy can be confirmed. The babies of women on social security and of those married to men in unskilled jobs are three times more likely to be born with these defects of the central nervous system than the babies of women married to men in professional jobs. The babies of top people are half as likely to die within the first week of life as the babies of people at the bottom of society, whose babies are also more likely to be dangerously small.[15] Small babies have a bigger risk of disability and greater vulnerability to illness.

As children grow, their health chances continue to be shaped by social and economic conditions. The children of people in unskilled jobs are twice as likely to die before they are fourteen than the children of parents in professional jobs. In general they have four times the rate of accidents, the cause of half the deaths of children over five. A quarter of the children who die between the ages of five and nine are killed by motor vehicles, and this is six times more likely to happen to children in social class five.[16]

For every child born dead, there are others who might have died and remain handicapped for life. For every one that has a fatal accident, there are others who are permanently disabled. As with death and chronic illness, disability is a class issue.

Our working lives compound the disadvantages sustained in childhood. After retirement the legacy of our work and our present social and economic conditions continue to be reflected in our health. Because people can no longer be categorized by occupation, less is known about the pattern of illness and death after people stop work. The class patterns of deaths from lung and stomach cancer, from bronchitis and infectious disease continue. The death rate for people in council housing remains higher than that among owner occupiers.

Women and men

Women go to the doctor more often, consume more medication, are admitted to hospital more often and are more frequently diagnosed as having psychiatric problems than men.[17] This may reflect a higher level of everyday health problems or less reluctance to go and see the doctor than among men. Even so it seems likely that women suffer at least as much chronic illness and probably more mental health problems than men. When it comes

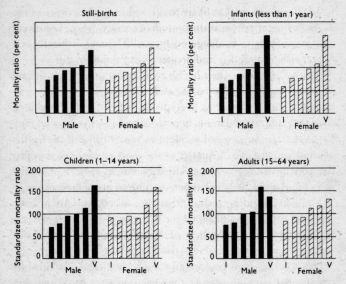

Figure 6. The class pattern of death throughout life. Source: *Occupational Mortality 1970–1972* (HMSO, 1978), p. 196.

to how long women live, however, the picture is very different. Women's death rates at all ages are substantially lower than men's and on average they live six years longer.

In general the class differences among married women are less extreme than among men. But this is not true of single women. The death rate among single women under sixty-five who work in administrative and managerial jobs is less than half of that of single women who work in the chemical industry, or hospital workers or textile workers. The death rate among the very few single women who become top civil servants or M Ps is a quarter of that of single women who work in small clothing factories. Our health is shaped as much by our circumstances as our biology. Because diagrams of class differences in female mortality do not show such extremes as diagrams of male mortality, another important fact about them tends to get overlooked. The diagrams for men show a stepwise gradation with social class, but the diagrams for women tend to fall into two clear blocks. For women the manual/non-manual split is sharper than for men.

It is frustrating that our glimpses into the patterns of women's morbidity and mortality are based only on knowledge of their husband's job if they are married. There are so many other factors potentially affecting our health: whether we have children, how old they are, whether we go out to work, whether we do a full-time or part-time job; and very little is known about the influence of any of these. There is some evidence that women who go out to work in general experience better health,[18] but this is dependent on other factors, including whether they also carry the burden of childcare and domestic work. The study in Camberwell found the highest levels of depression in working-class women with children under six. More than three in ten of such women were found to be clinically depressed.

Higher mortality rates among single, widowed and divorced people than among married people have led some epidemiologists to see marriage as a 'protective factor' against illness.[19] They have also noted that the differences are substantially higher among men than among women. Marriage seems to be healthier for men than for women. The differences are particularly high in the middle years and become smaller in older age groups. In 1972 divorced and widowed men aged forty-seven had twice the death rate of their married counterparts, while widowed or divorced women of the same age had a 50-per-cent higher death rate. Studies have shown that death rates among men go up substantially in the six months following bereavement.[20] There are, however, considerable difficulties in the general interpretation of these statistics. It may be that among those who do not marry there are more unwell people.

Looking at the interaction between women's conditions of life and their marital status is intriguing, although the statistics available to us at present are based on low numbers. Analysis of statistics from the *Longitudinal Study* indicates that class differences persist whatever women's marital status. They also indicate that women who have never married have marginally lower mortality rates than women who are or who have been married, particularly in later years.[21]

Table 2 *Standardized mortality ratios of women by means and marital status*

	Single	Married	Widowed	Divorced
Owner occupiers with a car	79	85	103	92
Council tenants without a car	106	124	108	129

Source: unpublished tables from the OPCS *Longitudinal Study* (with thanks to Kath Moser).

Into the future

Along with the myth of diseases of affluence and the myth that illness and disability strike indiscriminately, there is a third myth. We are led to believe that society is smoothly making progress towards the better life and that the problems which afflict us now will fade with time and technological change.

Yet there is no evidence that class differences are narrowing or even that the everyday health of most people is improving. In the past twenty or thirty years the fall in mortality rates which occurred in the earlier part of the century has begun to level out. Since 1949 the greatest fall in death rates has been among people at the top of society. Indeed for men in social classes four and five the death rate has actually risen.[22]

We do not know how the class pattern for specific illnesses is changing over time. The most recent information available for

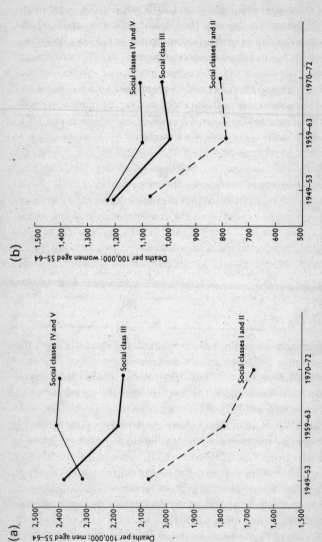

Figure 7. Changing death rates for women and men by social class.
Source: derived from *Inequalities in Health: The Black Report* (1982).

most conditions is for the period 1970 to 1972. So as yet there are no figures on the way the present economic crisis which began in the mid-seventies is shaping our health. We do know, however, that in the population in general, deaths from cancer (particularly breast and lung cancer in women), cirrhosis of the liver, suicide and mental disorders are on the increase. People are also taking more days off work sick and report more acute and chronic illness to the *General Household Survey*. Between 1971 and 1978 spells of time off work increased by 14.6 per cent for men and 32 per cent for women.[23] Between 1972 and 1980 there was a 45-per-cent increase in people reporting long-standing health problems to the *General Household Survey*.[24]

It may also be significant that the problems people experience seem to fit less and less into the conventional diagnostic categories. Between 1971 and 1978 the increase in people going off work for 'symptoms and ill-defined conditions' increased by 23 per cent among men and 50 per cent among women. For both women and men, illness without a clear diagnosis constitutes, after flu and chest infections, the most common reason for time off work.

Class conditions

Official statistics do not tell the whole story, and they leave many unanswered questions. But they are thought-provoking and provide a starting-point for considering what makes us ill. They tell us that there is something seriously wrong with the view most of us acquired in childhood that illness is a kind of natural disaster.

How healthy or unhealthy we are is evidently closely tied up with our work and home lives. Statistics cannot tell us the nature of that connection, but they provide dramatic evidence of how far-reaching it is. There have always been a few illnesses which people have recognized as linked to social conditions: tuberculosis, miners' diseases like pneumoconiosis, children's illnesses like rickets. Recently the asbestos-related diseases, particularly mesothelioma, an otherwise rare form of cancer, have come to people's attention. But what we learn from the official evidence is that there are in fact very few conditions which occur more frequently in people with better conditions of life. Whether it is everyday problems you might not even go to the doctor with, like headaches, back pain or depression, debilitating complaints, like varicose veins or ulcers, major conditions such as epilepsy or diabetes, chronic recurrent illnesses like bronchitis, disabling conditions which develop later in life from deafness to rheumatoid arthritis, common major life-threatening illnesses like kidney disease, heart disease, strokes and cancer, or rarer illnesses like meningitis, our chances of avoiding them depend upon our class position.[25] The likelihood of our babies being born dead or handicapped, the possibility that they may die in the first few weeks of life and the risk they run of being killed by cars or in other accidents are also linked to our life circumstances.

The commonly held view that the connection between illness and social conditions is a thing of the past is evidently nonsense. It is true that infectious diseases which were more common among the poor and killed them more often – and are still major killers in the Third World – have almost died out in Britain. It is also true that modern illnesses, in particular diabetes, high blood pressure, cancer and heart disease, are more prevalent in industrial societies, where living standards are generally higher, and for this reason are sometimes incorrectly described as 'diseases of affluence'. But the modern diseases which have replaced the infectious diseases are no more diseases of the rich in Britain than TB, smallpox or diphtheria were.

The health enjoyed by people at the top of society cannot be regarded as an absolute standard. Under different circumstances their health might be better too. But the knowledge that some people enjoy significantly better health than most people does give us an indication that we could experience less chronic illness and fewer untimely deaths. At the moment the gap between how it might be and the level of health which most people experience is growing. But the point of describing the stark class contrasts in illness and death rates in Britain today is not simply to chronicle a tragedy. The point about the gap between the health of the people at the top of society and that of the majority of people is that it is the evidence that things do not have to be as they are. The health at present enjoyed by some people should be the right of all.

Illness and death bring fear and grief. Modern illnesses, particularly cancer, are a source of anxiety for many people. But in a strange way knowledge of the class pattern of ill health can be an antidote to fatalism and resignation. It tells us our present suffering is not inevitable. Fewer women, men and children need die prematurely. There could be less chronic and recurrent illness. Our problems are less a matter of biology than of politics. Better health is possible.

2 Some Causes: Research and People Talking

Why do we get ill? What makes us well? How can we account for the present pattern of illness and death, with its stark class contrasts? What is the nature of the connection between the work we do, the money we earn, where we live, how often we get sick and the kinds of illnesses we suffer?

Because we tend to think of illness as either caused by germs or coming out of the blue, all the different ways in which our health reflects our environment are rarely at the forefront of our minds. Yet many modern illnesses are less of a mystery than we sometimes imagine. We know that heart disease is linked to high blood pressure, increased levels of cholesterol in the blood, smoking, diet – particularly fat and sugar consumption – and lack of exercise. Among researchers there is controversy about the relative importance of these factors and the proportion of deaths they account for, but at least we have some clues about possible connections, particularly with diet and stress. Cancer, surprisingly, is also now acknowledged to be a product of our environment. It is now accepted that four out of five cancers are environmental in origin. Cancer is known to be caused by a range of toxic substances, known as carcinogens, which are either inhaled or ingested or come into contact with the skin. Smoking, industrial chemicals, like asbestos and vinyl chloride monomer, and diet, including food additives, have all been implicated. In addition some researchers believe that many more modern organic chemicals may be proved to be major causes of cancer in coming years. It is also possible that substances may act in combination to cause cancer. Chloride ions and formaldehyde, for instance, produce BisCME, one of the most lethal carcinogens known.[1] Again there is fierce controversy about the relative importance of these factors. Some academics believe smoking is *the* most crucial cause.[2] Others argue that the role of industrial processes has been vastly underplayed.[3] But both sides are agreed that the possibilities for preventing cancer have been seriously under-rated. Respiratory diseases have also of course been linked with smoking, but pollution, industrial dusts and housing conditions are also important factors.

There has been less work done on the causes of non-fatal illness. But we do know, for instance, that skin conditions are often linked to contact with household or industrial chemicals, that hearing is damaged by excessive noise at work, that bronchitis and respiratory infections are aggravated by damp, that hypothermia is caused by excessive cold, that digestive problems, from constipation to diverticular disease, are linked with diet, and diet may also be implicated in all kinds of other conditions from headaches to kidney stones.

As well as linking our health to our environment, research also highlights why some living and working environments are more harmful than others. Factory and other industrial work frequently involves exposure to vibration, radiation, abnormal temperatures as well as noise, noxious chemicals and dangerous machinery.[4] Shiftwork, particularly rotating shift systems, which involve a kind of perpetual jet lag, has been shown to give rise to nervous disorders, digestive problems and ulcers.[5] Living in flats carries a higher risk of accidents, depression, anxiety and respiratory infection in women and young children.[6] Damp housing has been linked with bronchitis, asthma and other chest diseases.[7] People in overcrowded homes have been shown to be more likely to contract pneumonia, TB and other infectious diseases and to suffer more seriously with them.[8] Infant mortality rates are also higher in overcrowded housing and homes with shared bathrooms and toilets.[9]

People living in densely populated industrial areas of cities also live with greater levels of atmospheric pollution. Although heavily smoke-laden air has become a thing of the past, waste products from vehicles, factories and chemical works continue to be hazardous. Sulphur dioxide and other pollutants can contribute to the development of emphysema, asthma and chronic bronchitis. Lead can affect the nervous systems of young children, giving rise to irritability and lack of concentration, and it has also been linked to foetal abnormalities.[10] Apparently harmless chemicals emitted in small quantities can combine to produce substances which may cause cancer. There is evidence, for instance, that iron oxide in the atmosphere mixed with industrial dusts, like silica, can cause lung cancer.[11]

Researchers have been interested in the health effects of unemployment. Being out of work has been associated with increased incidence of depression, suicide, cirrhosis of the liver and raised blood pressure.[12] Death rates for children under five are also higher in the families of the unemployed.[13] In many ways men becoming unemployed experience the psychological damage which women not going out to work have known for years.[14] Tranquillizer usage certainly seems to be higher among both women and men who do not have a steady job outside the home.[15]

There are few diseases which have not been linked to what we eat, although there are endless controversies about the links between particular foods and particular diseases. It has been reasonably established that diets including high amounts of fat, sugar and refined foods and small amounts of fruit, vegetables and roughage are linked with digestive problems, bowel cancer and heart disease and may lower our resistance to illness. In addition, obesity increases the risk of heart disease, high blood pressure, diabetes, arthritis and complications of pregnancy.[16] Additives to processed foods may also turn out to be harmful. The dietary causes of slow, chronic illness are hard to detect, but there are additives banned in the United States which continue to be used in Britain, for example the colouring amaranth, which has been linked with cancer, miscarriage and birth defects.[17]

High perinatal and infant mortality rates are also often linked to nutrition.[18] From the government's yearly *Household Food Consumption* survey[19] we know that households on high incomes eat more health-giving and fewer health-damaging foods than people in low-income households, including twice the amount of fruit, a third more fresh vegetables, half the amount of white bread, nearly half the amount of sugar, and fewer cereals, potatoes and processed meat and vegetables.

Table 3 *Food consumption in rich and poor households, 1980 (ounces per person per week)*

	Gross income of head of household over £250	Gross income of head of household under £67
Processed meat	9.84	14.22
Fresh fruit	32.10	15.21
White bread	12.18	26.71
Sugar	7.78	12.21
Fresh vegetables	35.86	25.50
Processed vegetables	7.05	12.75

Source: *Household Food Consumption and Expenditure 1980* (HMSO, 1982), Table 20.

We all know smoking causes lung cancer, and we are beginning to be aware that it is linked with many other problems, including heart disease. What few of us realize, however, is that the risk of getting cancer is increased when smokers are also exposed to other industrial carcinogens. The risk to smokers exposed to asbestos, for instance, is greater than the simple addition of the risks of each on its own. There are more smokers among working-class men and women than among professional people. Working-class people also smoke more cigarettes a day on average. One in five professional people now smoke, compared with two in five women and three in five men in social class five. The class difference in cigarette consumption, however, has not always been so marked, and the evidence is that working-class people are finding it harder to give up. While one in three professional people has given up smoking in the past decade, the same numbers of working-class women are smoking as ever.[20]

Smoking has of course been linked to stress, as has overeating. Stress is a complex term and is often used in a catch-all way for emotional factors in illness. Nevertheless, strictly used it refers to a definite physiological state. Although brief periods of stress do not appear to be harmful, repeated or prolonged stress has been shown to result in damaging changes in the heart and blood vessels, including raised blood pressure, cholesterol and tendency for the blood to clot. It has also been linked to changes in the body's immune system. The number of illnesses in which stress is thought to be a factor increases all the time. As well as having a role in mental illness, heart disease and ulcers, stress may also increase susceptibility to cancer and infections, including flu and pneumonia.[21] Stress also increases our likelihood of having accidents at work[22] and in the home.[23] It has also been linked to complications of pregnancy, and it has been suggested that prolonged prenatal stress may change the body's biochemical balance in a way which blocks the abortion of malformed foetuses.[24]

The relative contribution of all these factors to morbidity and mortality rates is a matter of speculation and continuing academic controversy. Little is known, too, about how the different causes, like diet and stress, interact. It is also unclear to what extent all of these factors together account for the general pattern of illness and death. The researchers in the Whitehall study in which top civil servants were found to have four times fewer fatal heart attacks than men in unskilled jobs obtained confirmation that the incidence of heart disease is linked to higher blood pressure, smoking and lack of exercise. But what is interesting is that when all these factors were added together they still accounted for less than 40 per cent of the difference in death rates. The researchers concluded that even when all the possible known causes of heart disease are taken into account, three in five deaths from heart disease cannot be explained. There must be other reasons, they argue, why the men in the unskilled jobs suffer so disproportionately.

It is relatively easy to study the quantifiable aspects of people's lives: whether they smoke, how much they eat of different kinds of foods, how many people per room there are in their house. But many facets of our lives are more difficult to study by the established epidemiological methods. The tangled web of forces, circumstances and relationships which surround us are not always amenable to controlled studies or multiple regression analysis. To balance what we understand from research with what we can learn from experience, I went to listen to eight women and men who have each thought a lot about life and health. The aim was to explore how the known environmental factors bear on our lives in practice, to see how they interact, to look at what might be involved in the chronic stress we are told can damage us in so many ways and to find out about some of the less measurable influences on our wellbeing.

The interviews all took place in early 1983, before the June election. Each statement is an edited transcript of an hour and a half's conversation. I knew Vera Mitchell and Shan Jagedo already. The others were introduced to me by people we know in common.

Time factors: Shan Jagedo

I was making time switches. I worked there since 1970. The factory made all kinds of industrial instruments to time anything: your central heating, your radiators, your television, your coffee machine. I used to be a repairer, repairing all kinds of rejected work.

In 1974 I went on to the assembly side. They said it was because of a reduction in repair work. But that was an excuse. It was because of the equal pay that they got rid of women from the repair section and put them on assembly work. I fought like hell. I got the union in there and everything, but the union did not back me.

What the assembly workers used to do was to assemble the components to complete the instrument. If the instrument is big it can be in three parts or more, but by making the instrument small, one person can complete the whole job. It was women who did the work. There were a few men, but not on assembly.

The repair job was the kind of work you are not bored in. You are doing something. You are not controlled by a foreman or management because *you* have to make that thing go. You are the boss. Nobody could tell you how to make it work. It was interesting.

Assembly work is time-loss. You go there and you are just doing one thing. You are learning nothing. You just put things together. And it also meant a cut in my wages as well. By going on the assembly I lost about £5 a week. Even then I fought, but the union said you have to accept less money on the assembly.

The women's main complaints were about the piece-work rates or if the components did not fit properly. But you did not hear many complaints. Women don't tend to complain much. But they did complain if it was too hot or too cold or if the components were not flowing. If you haven't got the components you just sit there on waiting time. They only pay you a flat rate for that waiting time. The flat rate is only half the usual hourly rate, including the bonus.

There were bitter complaints. The women went on strike. They struck for lack of components, for the cold and for losing their bonus. The factory was so cold you could not hold anything. It was freezing, zero. That place is like a stable and when the wind blows it comes through the roof. The women took the strike in their own hands.

Eventually within five hours we got four or five heaters. Only one department of about thirty women went on strike. The others said they were not cold. But when the heating was fixed everybody benefited. Women tend to get very discontented fighting for something, and if nobody supports you, you become the troublemaker. They got fed up, and some left. Others retired or were made redundant. Now that militancy has been lost. The militant period was from 1971 to 1974. After that I was the only shop steward left.

Many women were sick in the place. But people do not think their illness is created from the factory. But my strong belief is it is there where all your illness comes from. Most of the illnesses they had were like flu, flu, flu. Some had migraine, headache, you name it, everything. They also had shoulder ache because when you are using a machine operated by compressed air you have to press down. Some got chest pain. They had the feeling that their chests were expanded when they were working. Then there was the jig machine, used for riveting. It was probably built in the seventeenth century or God knows when, and people were always getting their fingers trapped in it.

But people would say as an excuse 'I've got flu.' Now if you explain flu to somebody, they would not understand what flu you were talking about. I think it was the majority view that because you have got cold running down your nose you say 'I've got flu.' But it could be because they were run down, or from the compressed air, which blows dust up into your face, or the soldering fumes. Some used chemicals, thinners, and cleaning materials, and these can bring your sinus down.

Yes, I think the work was stressful. I mean all work is stressful. You just have to close your brain and try to make it happy. And think of Friday when you get your wage. Without that you can't live. When they are at home people are bored and then when they come into the factory they are bored. Then they become more depressed. There is no escape. Some were so depressed. Sometimes they would say they were going mad they were so depressed, especially if they had a lot of home problems too, like children or a sick family. Then coming to work they can't cope. The foreman puts pressure on them, saying they aren't making enough on piece-work. They are under pressure from the foreman, the management and the other workers. Yes, the other workers as well, because if they are doing part of the assembly work and the others are kept waiting, they do not produce enough to keep the others in work. When women are depressed, they get withdrawn. They can't take part in conversation and then sometimes they talk, talk, talk and suddenly cry.

Is it better to go out to work or to be stuck at home? If society was up to a certain standard life would not be just about escaping from the domestic world to the factory. If you think you can escape from the home into the factory you create two problems. If you stay at home all the time that is a problem by itself. It becomes boring. You overwork yourself doing the same thing over and over. But I would not say that to escape from home into the factory is better. You are worse off. You are doubly worse off. That's what I experience. Truly experience. Especially in industrialized countries.

Where I come from, when you escape from home you really feel happy working. You work among men, and when men get a dollar, you get a dollar, because remember it is agriculture. You do not see this male and female wage. You work side by side and it is totally different. You enjoy yourself. Although the work is hard you can have some happiness. When you come home you remember your friends. A good working environment can take your weariness off. You have a joke and a laugh and there is no foreman chasing you. If he chases you, then you put your tools down and they can't afford that, because in agriculture the product spoils. But in the factory if you put your tools down, they can afford it. They lose profits, but metal does not spoil.

I used to plant rice, working in the fields. Rice is a craft job. You have to be good or they won't hire you. You work from half past seven in the morning to two in the afternoon. All you eat is fruit. You can't walk back through all those miles and miles of water to come back and eat. You work in water, but because the sun shines and the water gets warm, it is okay. Just like anything else, if the rice field is there, you become a rice planter or a rice cutter. If the factory is there making cars, you become a car worker. A job is a job, but I used to love it. One thing good about it was it kept you healthy. Your whole body became exercised. Maybe it was because it was a warm country. Maybe I was young and I didn't feel it, but I can tell you I never got backache until I came over here.

Also, there were nicer feelings in the fields than in the factory. There were very nice feelings in the rice field. Maybe it is because in the factory you have to keep an eye on the machine, or else you could get caught in it and chopped to pieces. In the rice field the only thing you will find is a water snake or something like that. It is less worrying, less tense. Unless of course people have domestic problems, like kids, husband, in-laws when you are married. But women at home will fight back. It is rare they let that pressure dominate them.

The rice field was like piece-work, you had to work fast, but if, say, a hundred people have to plant out five acres of rice, the hundred people worked as a group. When you plant you go backwards, and when you see you are nearly finished you cut into other people's work. You say 'I am going to do some of your work, so you try to catch me up,' and then people come out equal. It is harmony.

I can only talk from my experience. The rice industry was different from the sugar industry. The sugar industry was controlled by Tate and Lyle. My father worked in the sugar industry. It was extreme exploitation. There was unemployment too, because the political situation changed. The other side destroyed the vegetation and land, and the ordinary people started to suffer. One time when the political situation got hot they threw oil in the sea so that people could not catch the fish to eat. So you do have nasty things happen.

When it comes to comparing the quality of life, at least over there you could have three meals a day. Here, although you get your money, everything is hurry. There is no time to have a decent meal at home. Here there is hassle all the time. Hurry because of the system, clocking in and clocking out. At home there is time to get some leisure. There, breakfast is not just a slice of toast; we have roti and split peas, like soup. Relaxing to eat a meal is a different way. When you work in the fields you have time for three meals a day and lots of fruits in between, like mangoes, guava and papaya.

There is a higher standard of living in Britain, but what do you enjoy from it? I mean I do not finally enjoy to become like a prisoner. You are tied to things. If you say I am going to take an hour and just forget about things, you can't afford to do it. There is an hour ahead waiting for you. And when you try to catch up the hour you lost, you try to do two hours' work in an hour.

We are prisoners in the home. When I go home, all I do is stay at home. Even if you have a couple of hours and you want to be with friends, there is not much time to socialize, because of the next day ahead of you. I make life a bit happy at the weekend, but even then if you are active doing other things, you have no weekend at all. In the factory where I used to work, the women do overtime and work on Saturdays, otherwise they would not get their money, because the wage is so low and they need to make ends meet. On weekdays they work from 7.30 a.m. to 4.45 p.m., and some stay an extra hour. Then on Saturdays the hours were 7.30 to 11.30. I myself worked Saturdays so that ends would meet.

In 1980 they took me off assembly and put me on to soldering. I was asked to practise the soldering. For two continuous hours I soldered and then I collapsed and was taken to hospital. The hospital did not understand what happened. All they were looking for was whether my blood pressure was up. They said I must have rest, but they did not know what caused my high blood pressure. Probably they are so ignorant themselves they do not know that soldering fumes can trigger illness. All they want to know is how to take out somebody's heart and put in another heart. They do not care about common illness.

The factory doctor said if I returned to work I might feel better. But instead of getting better I got worse. I lost my taste and my memory was going. I could not concentrate on the job, which needed concentration. My eyes were weak and my nose was running. I had no air to breathe and my mouth was dry. Then, after the dryness, my mouth started dripping water. It was dripping and I couldn't speak. So I put my foot down and said I am not going to continue under these conditions. The union suggested I should wear a mask, but I was a real fool with the mask, because it did not do anything. Then I just lost my sense of humour and said 'Don't bring this rubbish to me.' The other women wanted to support, but they tend to think 'I'm not sick, why should I care?' But they were wrong. Everyone was suffering with cold. Just because it does not show up as a serious illness, it does not mean they are not sick. You are burning metal. You are breathing poison all the time. And that was it. I refused to work under those conditions and I was sacked.

When I was sacked, I was looking round for jobs and could not find one. Although it paid £20 a week less, I finally found one through the Jobcentre. This factory made parts for cars and tractors, for instance for Ford. There were eleven women working on the assembly side, and five worked in the press shop. Unlike the other factory this was physically heavy work. The work was more exhausting as well as boring and dangerous. I worked in the press shop operating a huge press. Was I tired? Extreme tired. I could hardly reach the machine. On one machine when the guard closed, it touched my chin. And the lighting was poor. Although there was oil and grease all over the machines, washing facilities were poor. There was one toilet with cold water for the women, just in a zinc shed outside.

You needed a lot of concentration, because if you did not put the metal properly in the press, you would break the machine. At the same time you had to go with speed, because it was piece-work and if you didn't do it at the necessary rate you got the sack. The governor said you had to do 500 and then you would be paid bonus for the rest, but I never did 500. I never did more than 250. I couldn't cope with the job. There was a lot of pressure on us in both jobs, but at least in the first factory it was controlled a bit by the union. But in this other factory, only the skilled men, the craft workers, were in a union.

The women accepted the conditions, because as Asian women coming into the country they could not get jobs. They would say they are lucky this boss is so kind and gives them work. They said they used to be very tired, but as time went by they became hardened to the job. However, when you see the women and the machines, I don't know how they managed it. I don't think I could ever get used to it. Maybe you just have to come to work and put off feeling the aches and pains. But later when you go to bed, you can't help feeling the pain.

The effect on my health was tiredness, mental, physical and every-thing. My whole body used to pain. Every day I was dirty. As soon as I got home I could not do anything but get in the bath. Dirt. Dirt. Dirt. My whole front from my chest to my stomach was soaked with grease every day. The machine oil and grease came right through my clothes.

I lasted fifteen weeks. I had hoped to organize a union. They said I lost my job because of the slump in the car industry.

At the moment my health is pretty fair, but one thing that has happened is that I have developed dermatitis. It seems like this is incurable. It was probably caused by grease and oil and having your hands covered with gloves and getting sweaty. The doctors also say I have blood pressure problems. It was first noticed by the doctor in 1974 and now he says that it will be dangerous if I do not take the tablets. I think when you are active and fighting for things and you try to get across your message and your message is not heard, this will build your hypertension. Hypertension is not a disease to load tablets into people. What do the multinationals who make drugs in factories know about health? Some people may benefit from the tablets, but others do not need them. They need relaxation and to campaign for a better life.

Temporary tenant: Les Bennett

There is a chain reaction. When people become ill their problems increase. The conditions under which people exist deteriorate. I use the term 'existence' rather than 'living' deliberately, because it is not living as far as I am concerned. Bad housing is in itself responsible in many cases of bronchial and chest trouble, and also for stress and strain. But I have found from personal experience that ill health also results in bad housing.

Both myself and my eldest son have been hospitalized with TB – he in one ward and me in another. You could almost say it was heritage. My father himself died of TB and I have had it from childhood.

I was working for Bristol Siddeley. One of its subsidiaries, Hawker Siddeley, opened a new factory in Blackpool to produce Hunter Hawker aircraft. So I went with the company and stayed there for several years. I didn't have any TB in Blackpool. I think it was the fresh air. Healthwise I was much better up there. When the factory closed I decided to pick up the threads and start again. We returned from Blackpool to Coventry, where I was born and bred. This was some twenty years ago.

We were homeless. The only accommodation offered by the council at that time was one room in which myself, my wife, my son and my youngest daughter had to live and sleep. The council was made aware that I was a pulmonary tuberculosis case by the consultants at the Coventry and Warwickshire Hospital, but it did not make any difference. The room was part of an old workhouse building in Coventry, certainly no place for people suffering from TB to be with others in the family. The boy was five or six at that time. My daughter was nine months old. These were the days when Coventry was meant to be a boom town. There should have been no housing shortage.

We were in one room for about eighteen months. We had to cook, eat, sleep and everything else in it. I was still receiving treatment from the Outpatients at the hospital. Then, because the council was pressurized by the consultants at the hospital, they did offer us a place in Radford. The new house was damp. It could only be said at best that it was better than what we had had before. We lived there for ten years.

Because of my state of health, the doctors would not allow me to work. So we were living on state benefits. Due to high heating costs and inadequate benefits, and in common with many, many others through-out the city, we found ourselves getting into arrears of rent. So we were given notice to quit, and in 1976 were put into what was called a 'temporary tenancy'.

This 'temporary tenancy' was in a deplorable state of disrepair. There was rampant damp, falling plaster, draughts through every door, and no inside toilet. One or other of us suffered with coughs and colds all the time. There was also the danger, of course, that it might bring a flare-up of the old TB. My youngest son, who was ten at the time, also had chest troubles. As a result he was sent to an open-air school just outside Coventry. With losing a lot of time from school, he got behind. That in turn became an emotional problem as well as a medical one. He felt inferior because he was not able to keep up with school work. There is no end to what can come out of all these things.

The biggest part of our married lives, bar for the short time I was working for Hawker Siddeley in Blackpool, has generally been spent penny-pinching, trying to manage on an income below the poverty line. It was the adversities we had to go through and the general conditions we had to live under at that time that made me campaign for better conditions for people who were in similar circumstances. There were at least a hundred temporary tenancies throughout the city. The people put in them were in similar circumstances to myself. People who had suffered ill health over a long period or were unemployed or whose marriages had broken up, and could not afford the rent or council mortgage repayments. There were cases where children received second or third-degree burns because paraffin heaters were being used, because of the high cost of fuel. I have been in houses where the wallpaper has been thumped at, nailed up in some instances, because ordinary adhesive would not hold. If you put it up at night it would be on the floor by the morning. There were cases where whole families had to live, eat and sleep in one room because the bedrooms themselves were reeking with damp. Ill people would be sleeping among the rest of the family because the only way to maintain any heat at all was in the one room. They would huddle in there. As many as six, seven, eight people I have seen in these conditions.

The Trades Council did a survey of all the temporary tenants, and the results were absolutely shocking. So much so they called together a meeting. They put leaflets out and put the word about to get all these temporary tenants together to see what they themselves thought of the idea of forming an association and fighting for better conditions. Eighty or ninety tenants came. A steering committee was elected and we were under way. It developed into a major campaign, the like of which has never been seen in this city before. We made terrific progress. We took three test cases to the high court, and it was ruled that the council was guilty of putting people in premises which were detrimental to the health of the occupant. Now there are provisions which prevent the council moving one tenant out of a house deemed unfit and moving another one in. Because of our efforts, 103 families were rehoused. Which just goes to show that if people really get together and act together, something can be done. We were really over the moon when we won. Now we have set up a tenants' federation for the whole city. We are a sort of umbrella organization. Our aim is to build more and more associations throughout the various areas of the city who can fight for better conditions.

Following the three-year 'temporary tenants' campaign our house was finally sold to a housing association. They rehoused us. Now we have a fairly decent property. I would not say it is 100 per cent, but then I have yet to find a 100-per-cent house. But it is dry. And the thing is, if it is dry, you can do something with it.

Since we have moved, my health has been very much better. In the two years I have been in the house we are in now, I have had a clean bill of health from the hospital. This is the point. It proves it. I am not susceptible to colds any more. Of course I get the odd cold, because I am just that little bit weak, and my chest is the weakest point. Whereas before I was hardly free of a cold, and the rest of my family as well, we now find we don't get this. Like everybody else, if we have a cough or a cold it comes and goes. We can get rid of it. Before, it used to hang on, because of the conditions. Whatever medical help you got or medicines you took, it did not do you much good, because you were still within the environment of dampness. My son is better, too. His school is a beautiful place out in the country. They get fresh air and regular meals. He has come on a bomb since then.

Even now, although the TB has gone I suffer with my chest and have a bit of difficulty getting about. I must be honest about this. It must be in part due to the fact that I smoke. I would not say I am a heavy smoker, but I would not call myself a moderate smoker either. It must have some effect. It does affect my breathing. In a general sense I find I am able to get around more than I did. When it was at its worst it would be a hell of a fight to get up a hill. You had to stop two or three times to get your breath. It made life very miserable. I think that far less people would smoke if they were not under stress and strain, as the average tenant is today through unemployment, marital problems and so on. Picking up a cigarette and having a draw, knowing it perhaps could do you harm, does not deter you. It becomes as Valium to a person who is undergoing sleepless nights. As Valium helps you overcome that, so a cigarette helps you overcome stresses and strains. I feel that if such anxieties and pressures were not on them, far more people would give up smoking.

In Coventry there are still temporary tenants, but they are not known as temporary tenants, because during our campaign we got that wiped out. In other cities the same thing is going on. They are herding people together in some form of ghetto, and they are looked on as second-class citizens because, through no fault of their own, through unemployment, marital problems, marriage break-ups, they have got into rent arrears. They are driven into these rat-holes and then despised for being there. They are at the bottom of the pit, and their limited income does not give them sufficient margin to be able to clamber out. It only gets worse. They get further and further in. Compassion goes by the board. As regards Coventry council, people who get into rent arrears are placed into what are termed 'hard to let' estates. It is the same thing as in the days of the temporary tenants, but they are now given a different title. They are given notice to quit. They are fetched out. Then they are reallocated a flat in an area which virtually nobody else will take. No longer is their rent book overstamped 'temporary tenant', but they are still living in temporary tenant conditions. Whereas we had 103 temporary tenants, there are now over a thousand in 'hard to let' premises. And council statistics show that each day, each month that goes by, rent arrears and mortgage arrears are increasing, hand in hand with the way unemployment is increasing.

It is obvious if a chap loses his job he can manage for a few weeks. His redundancy will keep him in the clear. But gradually money goes, and he comes on to benefit, which is not far short of the poverty line. And it hits him.

And if they pay the rent, they can't pay the electric and by paying the electric they can't get their food, and so it goes on. Soon a new government ruling will mean that tenants on social security will have their rent deducted at source. On the one hand this will reduce arrears to the council. On the other hand it deprives the recipients of the benefit of actually having control of their money. Before, they had the choice of paying rent, electric, gas or whatever, but by depriving them of this choice the screw tightens yet again. They have no choice. It's Hobson's. In this day and age everyone is juggling books, including big companies, the Bank of England and the government themselves. But they are able to do this. They are not deprived of the privilege of being able to juggle. But the tenant is.

For sick people it is worse. If you are unemployed, at least if you have your health and a job comes along, or you can turn your hand to a bit of moonlighting or whatever, it gives you some sort of chance. But sick people, they've got no choice, no chance.

I think the authorities should look to the general living conditions of people. The riots, like in Toxteth or Greater Manchester, are not brought about solely by unemployment but by other factors, housing being paramount. It is no wonder that kids today say 'Why should that person have a decent house, when mine is in such a diabolical state that I am ashamed to take my mate home?' So they put the nearest brick through the window, and that's it. That is their only way of drawing attention to their plight. I think a lot of the problems we are getting do not stem from the inability of the parents to control their children, but from the very fact of the environment and the conditions they are living in.

Some of the 'hard to let' estates were built before the First World War. They are really horrible. The brickwork has perished to such an extent that whatever they do it will be difficult to bring it up to standard. The answer is to send the bulldozer in and fetch the lot down. But the council are building very little, obviously due to problems from Westminster. It is cut, cut, cut. The same thing applies to repairs. The council are curtailed from doing modernizations, while in most cases it would need complete modernization to solve the problems. What they are doing instead is a series of cosmetic exercises.

The council admit they now have 17,000 properties which are damp or lacking facilities. Many of these are on estates built in the 1950s on the 'no fines' method. They were literally slung up. They have no cavity walls, on the theory that if you mix concrete and pebbles, the air bubbles will trap insulation. As a result the houses never warm up. It is easy to blame the tenants. But the fault lies in the first place in bad planning and bad construction – and then in the fact that maintenance work which needs to take place has not been done as it should have been done. Damp is the main problem, together with inadequate heating, faulty electrics and constructional defects. All this again results in high heating costs. To keep a decent body temperature, particularly for the old people to avoid hypothermia, is just impossible.

People have no hopes at the moment. It is a grim outlook. It snow-balls. Unemployment and bad housing are bed-mates; a man loses his job and through no fault of his own he finds himself in financial problems. In addition he may face mental strain, family upset and break-up of marriage. In many cases it becomes insurmountable. People cannot see any way clear. There is no way they can juggle figures. They have no prospects, no ways, no means without some organization or someone to do something about it.

Chemical reaction: Andrew Tree

I am the shop steward. It is a small factory, with just about a hundred union members, so we only have one steward. I work as a chemical operator.

We make ion exchange resin. It is used in hospitals and industry for purifying liquids. We are termed a heavy chemical industry. The type of chemicals we use are highly toxic and dangerous. Some are poisonous. But unfortunately it was not until 1974 or 1975 that I was able to prove from different sources that four or five of the chemicals were car-cinogens.

I used to be a miner and a corporal in the Royal Engineers. I started at the factory in 1962 and took over the job of shop steward in 1966. It took me a bit of time to gain experience in being a shop steward, but in 1968 I felt confident enough to go externally with problems such as health and safety.

It appeared to us from memory that so-and-so and so-and-so had died, and the deaths were all from cancer. Every year one or two or three people died of cancer. And most of them weren't yet fifty. It mainly started as lung cancer, but by the time they died their bodies were riddled with it. So the branch wrote to the TUC medical officer and asked him about it, sending a list of chemicals we use. The reply was that none of the chemicals would create a cancer problem.

What I did not know at the time was that there was a big campaign going on in America, which a person such as the TUC doctor should have picked up, concerning the chemical BisCME.[25] By 1966 tests on animals had shown that BisCME causes cancer in mice. By 1971 a team from New York university had found it to be one of the worst carcinogens in the world. I put this knowledge to the TUC doctor, who found out I was correct. He got in touch with the Health and Safety Inspectorate, who came down and did a mass survey of the site.

The Health and Safety Inspectors went round with the management, and their conclusion was that everything was pretty good. So I asked them to come round with me. In one place there was a lime slaking pit. They had never seen it before, and they still could not see it, because the amount of dust in the atmosphere was such that you could not see the plant or the operator. They also found fumes being breathed by some workers five times greater than the maximum permitted level. Of course the inspectorate told the management that they had to have the process altered. But these were minor points, because they did not pick up the major problem, which was BisCME.

Following complaints from the workers the company employed a specialist doctor to do a mortality study. He did not even look at women, although two had died; and he looked at the general area, not at the factory. So because the general death rate in the area from cancer is low, the cancer deaths were hidden in the overall death rate, and the doctor told the management there was no problem. In fact we did not see the report until many years later. It was kept from the workforce, in case it was challenged.

In 1972 a meeting was held for the factory workers, attended by the TUC doctor, a doctor from the Employment Medical Advisory Service and the Health and Safety Inspectorate. Every time the company has got in specialist doctors the purpose has been to reassure us. The TUC man said there was a lack of human evidence on BisCME causing cancer. He went on to find excuses why the factory was not at fault. He told us that the cancer was probably due to 'life-style', particularly smoking, even though the majority of people who died were not smokers. When he was asked by one of my members whether he would advise us to leave the factory, the TUC doctor said no, because the factory medicals at least let you know you have got cancer earlier than your doctor would. The workers' comment was unprintable. CME stands for chloromethylether, but we called it 'cold meat eventually'.

The doctors claimed I was a scaremonger. When in the course of talking to my members I said 'Look, for God's sake don't do what you are doing now, because it will bloody kill you', they would say 'Sandy, you are our shop steward, we expect you to talk to management, but bugger off now and let us get on with our work. The doctors and professors have told us there is nothing to harm us.'

Nevertheless the feeling started to get one of alarm. People started to say 'It can happen to us.' The factory inspectorate ordered a clean-up. What the management did was to put a chain-link fence around the CME plant! On top of that we still had CME going through open drains all through the factory. There were vats and reactors with lids open and chemicals swirling round inside. I once got told off by the works engineer because one of the men had left his mask in the plant. He told me the fumes in the atmosphere could collect on the mask and anyone who wore it would have their faces burnt. But when you think about it, this was the atmosphere that people were breathing in. All the management were concerned about, though, was physical injury you could see and claim compensation for.

Eventually they made the plant where the CME is added to a catalyst into a sealed building. But unfortunately, because of the highly corrosive nature of this chemical, it used to eat into the equipment which was meant to stop the CME getting into the atmosphere, and half the time it was not working. On top of that, a wall of a sealed building was smashed and never repaired, so fumes came out into the area where people were working. A fitter assistant had his air mask ripped off when he went to jump out of the way of a leak, and he had CME all over him. He is now disabled for life, with burns, hearing problems and an eye defect, and of course this does not take into account the possibility of future ailments.

If they wanted you to clean out a vessel which had had, say, ethylene dichloride or sulphuric acid in, you would just wash it down. We knew at the time it must be doing some harm, but of course we could not prove it. The men used to go to the nurse and ask for a jar of Vaseline. Although they were in a rubber suit they had to smear this over their

testicles, because it was the softest part of their body, and of course these
damn chemicals used to burn them. Sometimes you would run upstairs
carrying a bucket of chemicals with fumes trailing behind you. When
you had chucked it in, you would go to the wall where a hole had been
made and breathe in great gasps of air, because you had been holding
your breath all that time. What it puts me in mind of is this. In this
country in this day and age people are allowed to work in situations
worse than the gas chambers were in America. At least people were
guilty of murder there. These people are guilty of nothing, only wanting
a living, and yet they were working in gas-chamber-like conditions. The
gas chamber was quick. This is slow lingering death.

CME was introduced into the plant in 1954. The first bloke to die
was the chemist doing the research into its introduction. He died of lung
cancer in 1956. He was forty-seven. Another bloke had to clean out a
reactor. He had an air mask on, but some of the chemicals are absorbed
through the skin. He did not have any protection on the rest of his body,
and we had to physically lift him out because he collapsed in there. He
died of cancer five or six years later.

What proved to me it was a high-risk factory was the age of the people
that were dying. If you look at the national statistics on lung cancer for
that age group, you are looking at two in a hundred deaths. We had a
big lot of them. Throughout the country 20 per cent of deaths are from
cancer, which means that for every two dying of cancer you should have
eight dying of other causes. But by 1980 I had had twenty-four dying
of cancer and three dying of other causes. (And even one of these was
later found to have cancer, although I had been told it was a burst ulcer,
and because he was not a union member I was told to keep my nose out
of it.) So there was a great imbalance there. But what I couldn't
understand was why the hell I couldn't get any further with it. Facts
are facts.

In 1977 another company took over the factory and cleaned up the
process. Now CME is made in a sealed process, and we've got constant
monitoring. Immediate action is taken when you find the slightest
amount of contaminant. One of the main reasons they were prepared
to improve things was that they had already had a plant in America
where they had gone through this exercise anyway.

The Health and Safety Executive started an epidemiological study in
the early 1970s, but then abandoned it. They said they didn't bother

with it because they had accepted BisCME was a carcinogen. But what I am bitter about is that they did not bother to inform the workers that they had now decided we were working with a cancer-causing substance. In 1980 we finally got some epidemiological studies done, funded by the EEC. They confirm (i) that BisCME is a carcinogen, and (ii) that in our factory a lot of deaths were caused by this compound. The study gave us each a rating on how much contamination we had received. So, although the process has been cleaned up, you have still got that worry at the back of your mind. Some of the employees – and I am one of them – have a thirty times greater risk of being killed by cancer than somebody who never worked there. When we made a film for BBC Wales, a cancer specialist said on the programme that in the next twenty or thirty years we would continually have deaths occurring, because of the long latency period of cancer. A few people with a high rate of contamination have died, but there may be many more deaths in the next ten, twenty or thirty years.

Even for the healthy ones that are left, the mental anguish is terrible. We have X-rays once a year. If there is a shadow or anything on it you have to go back. Put yourself in that person's position. In some cases, between it being identified and dying there is a period of only three or six months. One bloke had to go into hospital for tests on his throat. To put it crudely, the bloke told me that when he was in there he was shitting himself because he was bloody scared. Fortunately it was nothing to do with cancer. They still do not know what is wrong with him, but at least they have alleviated the worry of cancer. Another person suffered a lot of pain in his back passage. It got so painful that the company found out about it and sent him off to the hospital. His biggest worry was that he might be like one of the people who died before. Then he found out it was piles. In my own case I was worried by a lump in my groin. I ignored it and ignored it. But then, when the doctor at the medical examination examined me it was a hernia. I can tell you it was quite a relief. Down in our factory we know that once we get cancer we do not live long.

Some people's wives nag them to get out from the factory. But round this area now, especially at this point in time when there is not a lot of industry and employment, they know even if they wanted to leave they couldn't. Of course we have achieved improvement. But still it took too long. It's wrong that it should all be up to a small group of people who have to spend a lifetime working on it. I think there are many carcinogens in factories and homes all over the country which have not been recognized. There is also the problem of chemicals interacting. I have not seen anywhere in the literature anything about what happens when ethylene dichloride which goes down the drains is mixed with an alkali, for instance, but it produces VCM, another powerful carcinogen. In our factory I am worried about standards sliding backwards. We might find that in six months' time more safety measures are needed and then it could be a case of 'What do you want: a place to work or out on the dole?'

Now my concern is to get compensation for the families of the people that have died. So far they have not got a penny. But sometimes I really get downhearted, because the subject is morbid. People even say 'Oh, here is Captain Death coming.' Not a nice thing. But you have to put up with it to try and get justice. I won't attend the funerals. I don't know why. Maybe I have got a guilty conscience that I failed that person. I don't know. All the families of the dead people know it was the factory. Some of them are very bitter. I went to see one widow, and she must have had it all bottled up. I can assure you I spent a very, very unhappy two hours with her. One of the problems was not breaking down myself. On the way home I had a sob in the hedge. She was a nice woman. We knew her, because she used to be one of the office staff. They picked it up early and removed a lung, hoping that would cure it. But unfortunately he had secondaries. So it lasted for about two years, and she had the problem of assuring him he was getting better right up to the last.

We were at the factory long hours. In those days the company expected us to be in work at seven in the morning and work through to six o'clock at night. You had to work all that time to get a living wage. During the dinner break, to relieve the monotony we used to have an old aluminium kettle. We used to pick sides and play ten minutes each way. I swear you would think it was the cup final. Whichever was top of the league at the end of the week used to have the kettle. Now all these blokes were fit. It is not as if they were doddery, overweight, fat people. They were just murdered. That is all I can say. It was murder in the name of making a profit. Time and time again I have accused the company of murder. They say 'You over-react.' Of course I over-react. They were my mates. I have spent a long time with them. Twenty-eight people have died, and more will die, and nothing has been done about it. The factory managers who were responsible at the time are still walking around free. And this is happening throughout industry today. It is inhuman. I wish society was different. But it seems that human life means nothing. I doubt if there will be much change in my lifetime, because I can't see human beings ever being allowed to tread the corridors of power.

Womb trial: Ruth Hutchinson

They are so snobbish at the school where I am doing my placement. There was a photographic session the other day and there were about thirty teachers there. The majority of the children are from ethnic minority groups, but there were only two black faces among the staff. One was a domestic and the other an Asian teacher. I am the only other black person there. I feel very bad because they all kept coming and asking 'Would you watch my class while we have the photos done?' And no one said to me 'Would you like your photo done?' I really felt sad, because I am there working like a nigger.

Before I went to college I was working at a community nursery for seven years. I went there when the nursery was one year old. They wanted a lot of dynamic workers to get it off the ground. I was just an ordinary assistant and I worked so hard and I pulled myself along until I was appointed deputy head. Then I worked even harder, night and day. Then the matron left and I applied for the matron's job, but I didn't get it. That really did freak me out. That really was the nastiest blow I have ever had in my life. They said I didn't get the job because I didn't have a nursery nurse's qualification. But the person who got the job in the end has no qualifications at all. She had never done anything with children.

Personally I have suffered a lot, healthwise. I was suffering for quite a long time with severe menstrual pain. For one week in four I would lie in a sleeping bag and bleed and bleed. I would go along to the doctors and say 'Look, doctor, this is not ordinary menstrual pain. I am forty years of age. I have lived with menstrual pain all my life. I must know the difference between ordinary menstrual pain and what is happening to me.' I said 'Can I go to the Tavistock Clinic or somewhere, because it might be psychological?' But they just pilled me off.

So I took the situation in my own hands. When my period was on, I went swimming and I went running in the park like a mad woman just to get rid of the pain. In the end I took to the bottle. I was buying a whole bottle of brandy when my period came on. I would just reach for the brandy bottle and go down into the sleeping bag like a little worm and just wrap myself up tight and bleed. And this would go on for a whole week. It was horror. I went camping one weekend and took myself away from the group and just sat in the bush and bled all night.

I was getting into a nervous wreck. My job was suffering, because I couldn't go to work for a whole week every month. And I couldn't cope with my own children, who were going through adolescence. I had got myself into a state where I was making myself ill by worrying about it. I began to think 'I don't know how much more blood I can lose before I die.' During the other three weeks I was so weak I could not cope with looking after the nursery children.

I had it seriously for two years. One Monday night it came on so really bad that I crawled down the stairs and out into the street and started screaming, because I was going mentally ill with it. And I was just screaming and screaming. And then my son came and got me back into the house. There was no brandy around. I just fell into my sleeping bag and curled up. I didn't get into bed because I needed to be tied up really close. It is bringing tears to my eyes just thinking about it. You would not know how sad it was.

And I thought, 'Well, I can't go on like this. I know this brandy is not doing me any good. Before long I will be treated as an alcoholic. I will be put away. It must be something psychological. I am not happy at work. Where is it coming from?' And the doctors would not listen to me. I am sure my body was reacting to my life. I had lost someone I was close to, but that was seven years before. I went to the nursery the same year he died and I devoted myself to the nursery. So the nursery took his place. I was terribly hurt I did not get the matron's job. I think that had a serious effect. I was working non-stop at the nursery, and no one was giving me any credit for my hard work. It was very frustrating. And the nursery was faced with closure, and we had to fight to keep it open. So we had that to contend with as well.

I had to live with the new matron. I had to show her how to do the milk forms. I had to show her everything. And then she would not let me have time off to attend union meetings. There were shop stewards' courses I was entitled to go to, and she would not give me the time off to go. Now a dominant woman had become a mouse. I had no mouth to speak with. And I was powerless. I could not do anything. So I think my body reacted to all the things around me.

I saw another man doctor, and then a lady doctor. But she said 'I can't examine you now, you should have made a double appointment.' What did I know of double appointments? By this time I was in a real state, because my heart had begun to beat faster than it should be beating. I am very good at observing changes, and I thought 'Well, if my heart now is beating and I am not running or anything, I must put it down to fear of what is going to happen next.' I stopped eating. All I was living for was the brandy to keep the pain out. Then I cried, and I decided 'I am not going back to see her', and I wrote to a doctor at King's College Hospital with five pages of notes describing my life from when I had my first period to date. I was surprised when the letter came back from him saying I should come and see him.

Well, he took me into hospital overnight and he examined me, and he said I had to have my womb out. I didn't take kindly to this, because I was not sure whether my need was physical or mental. When I went in to have it done, I could not bear the thought of it and I went home again. But in January 1982 it got so bad that I was collapsing everywhere. I remember I was in Jones Brothers one Friday morning. I went to get something for my college work. I just stood there and passed out, flooding the shop. And the next minute I woke up in the nurse's room. Then one day I was at my nursery placement, and they were all waiting for their dinners. And I went down to the kitchen to get them – this was February – and I just collapsed in a pool of blood. I couldn't fetch the dinners up. They were all sitting up there waiting for their dinner. They took me home by taxi and I thought 'Christ, I've got to get something done.' Then there was March to come, and I thought 'Oh, God, how can I face another month.' With all the pressures on me, I couldn't handle it any more. So I phoned the hospital and said I have to have it done.

Well, I went in on the Wednesday night. I pleaded with the doctor. 'Is there no alternative? Please do not cut me. Please do something. Do anything, treat me mentally, but do not cut me.' Then he said to me 'Black women do not like to have their wombs removed', and this other white lady behind the screen heard and said 'Excuse me, doctor, white ladies do not like their wombs removed either.' And then I said 'Well, if you are going to remove it, please let me see what it looks like.' He said I had a fibroid as big as a fist. I said I had read in a book that you could remove fibroids without cutting, but he said 'Well, you don't want any more children, blah, blah, blah.' Well, I didn't want any more children, but I did not want my womb removed either. Then I thought 'I can't face any more embarrassment of collapsing everywhere, so I will have it.' But I still think until this day my need was not physical.

As well as the pressure of college and not getting my matron's job, I had two teenage children and I was going through hell with them. They were both unemployed and just decided they were not going to do anything but play music all day long. I was also buying this house on the GLC's homesteading scheme. I was living in fear that I might be indebted to the mortgage company for ever and ever. On my salary I could not get a mortgage, so I had to pay a man a fee to get me a mortgage, so on top of finding the mortgage I had to find the fee. It was having no one to turn to. I think that was the greatest frustration. And racism. You are prejudiced against first because you are a woman, second because you are a black woman, and thirdly I am a single woman with two children. I am discriminated against in every area, so what chance have I got?

By and by, on Thursday the eighth of April 1982 they whipped my womb out. And I never saw what it looked like. And they never showed me the fibroid and I am quite upset, because I wanted to look at it. I wanted to see it, as is my right.

And the worse was yet to come. I was not in a hospital near where I lived, so I had no visitors. And having your womb removed is not something you go round telling everybody about. And I had just moved to a new house, so nobody knew me in my neighbourhood.

There I was in hospital across the river, with two children who unfortunately could not be bothered with an old mother. Nine days later they turned me out. They wanted to send me home on the Friday. I had had it done on the Thursday before. I said 'I haven't really got anywhere to go, because I have just moved into a new house and it is full of builders. The toilet is downstairs, but there is nowhere downstairs I can stay.' In the hospital I couldn't walk and I was mentally distressed. I was in the hospital alone, having had a major operation, with no visitors and nowhere to go. So they said they would keep me in till Sunday, but I said 'I will go home on Monday.'

My daughter took me home and looked after me for three days. She went home on Wednesday night. So Thursday, Friday, Saturday and Sunday I had no one to look after me. I couldn't walk. I didn't really have anything to eat, because there was no food in the house. I couldn't get my neighbours to help because I had just moved into a new area. On the Monday a leaflet came through the door with the numbers of the social services and all that. I phoned the social services, and they said I had to get a certificate, but my doctor would not give me one because he said he knew nothing about the operation. I could not get to the shops, and I felt like a little old lady, bent over. All this time my mental state was going further and further away. Finally I got another doctor, and in June, two months after the operation, they finally sent me to a convalescent home.

When I came back from the convalescent home I was still very down, and the builder was still working on the house. I did not have any money, so I rang up the social services. One Wednesday morning there was a terrible bang on the door. I crumbled down stairs and there was this very very black man, carrying a black bag, in a black suit, who said he was from the social security. I took him into the kitchen and he said 'I was expecting to find a sick woman. According to this letter you are a sick woman. You do not look sick to me.' And he kept looking round the place, and he said 'With a place like this you do not need social security to help you. You need a man. That is what you need.' He was so rude. But I would not break down in front of him.

By now, and I am not ashamed to say it, I was really starving. I had no money at all. I had to rely on friends bringing me food. You may say 'Well, I was having my house done up', but that was with money I had got when I was working, and it had all been given out. I was still waiting for the building grant, and my college grant had stopped because I was sick. All of this financial stress combined with my illness to put so much pressure on me that I even became aggressive towards my children.

Every day I was just getting up and crying. And I was in this state of madness for months and months. When I was well enough I started going to the library. But then I had to face coming back into the house.

I would walk all round the streets rather than come back into the house. I was so distressed and lonely and really not well that everyone I saw in the street I asked them to walk me back to my door, or to come in and have a cup of coffee. And yet as soon as they were gone I would get into this mental depression again.

What amazes me is the stress that illness puts on the whole family. Because society makes us suffer so much, it splits up the family relationships. My daughter will not come near me, perhaps because she feels guilty that she did not realize what I was suffering. And I stay clear of her. And my son has not got a job and I moan at him. It was a closely knit family, and it is splitting. I feel very bitter.

When September came I wasn't really well enough, but I wanted to go back to college because I needed the grant money and I wanted to get out. Eventually I had a friend who took me to the Isle of Wight for Christmas, and I had a good rest there. And then I got back on my feet.

I would like to stand on a soapbox and say 'Any woman who is contemplating having a hysterectomy should consider the mental strain of it, which they do not tell you about. And you should find out what it will do to your sex life too.' After all, it is all to do with hormones. I asked the doctor what it would do to my sex life and he said 'Oh, you will enjoy sex better', but I have not had the time or energy to find out yet. No one told me I would put weight on, either, which I have done, especially on my bust. Nobody said, 'You will suffer hot sweat and cold sweat.' And there were times when I found myself sweating an awful lot. I would want to say to women 'Do not have it until you have found out everything you want to know. Write out a questionnaire for yourself. Write down for and against.'

I was in pain and I did think I needed something done to me. I think I might have killed myself if nothing had been done. I think in the end I would have died because of the things I was taking. And the world would have said 'That black woman committed suicide because she could not cope with her college work, or because she had strained herself to buy a house and could not handle it. Or because she did not get the matron's job.' But I still feel if I had had an understanding doctor, she or he could have helped me along another line.

I remember the last lot of STs I bought. I bought this great bag of STs in Boots. I still keep it on the wall in the bathroom. I can't get rid of it. I keep thinking 'My womb is not there. I was born with it. It is mine and they have taken it away from me.' I am grieved. They took it away without trial. They should have tried me and said 'This is your sentence. We will take it away from you.' But they just said 'You will have to do without it.'

I am feeling better now. I want to go on to do more studying, to make up for what I did not have when I was younger. I have got a place at the London School of Economics to do a trade-union course, but I haven't got a grant yet. I have become a health freak. I am making sure I do not have to go to the doctor again. I drink milk. I don't eat sugar. I exercise non-stop, and I live out in the fresh air. As much as I possibly can I go camping. And I try not to look on the dark side of all the things that have happened to me, because I think if you are bitter inside it reflects in your health. So I am trying to bounce back. I will come back. I am alive.

Robot work: Baden Gough

Stress comes in different ways. In a mass-production factory there is the stress that is brought by repetitive work and boredom. Then there is the stress of being caged in doing a job which never changes from one year to the next.

It is a massive complex. It is the biggest factory in Europe. At the moment there are about 8,500 workers; 4,500 work on the production side, roughly half in machining and half in assembly. There are various health hazards within the welding areas, the paint-shop areas and the tyre stores, where there is a heavy rubber content. Then there are the vast machine shops where you are tied to time cycles because of the machines. The risks there include dermatitis, eye strain and the physical strain of lifting heavy weights or operating heavy machinery.

Then of course there are the assembly halls. It is easy for me to talk about, but how can I draw a picture in your mind? A large tractor is put together in a number of monotonous stages. A track, which is a moving carriageway, starts at one end of the assembly hall. It is probably something like three quarters of a mile long. And on to that track just comes the chassis of the tractor, the back axle and the engine. At each station coming down the track people put various parts on to it, until in the end there is a complete tractor. Branching off from that main track is what we call the sub-assembly stations. For instance, the instrument panel, like in a car, which has various clocks and indicators, well, that is sub-assembled. Now what goes down that track does not vary from day to day or year to year. So the person who is employed to put the speedometer in the dashboard probably puts two or three other things in at the same time, but it never looks any different, and he never moves from the same square foot of room he has at the same bench.

You think the track is hardly moving but when you have only got a few seconds to complete your operation you are against the clock all the time, and that builds the pressure up. The other thing is if you are not feeling well, or unfortunately you have got a stomach upset, you cannot leave your station until a relief comes in. For every gang of about fifteen men there is usually only one floater. So if someone has already gone to the toilet, the floater is standing in for him; so you have got just to stick it out.

There are all kinds of things that build into that chappie as well. If you have got a son or a daughter at home that is not well or playing you up, which is not unusual, you have got that pressure on you as well. Because the work is not completely mind-absorbing, your mind is always going back to your worries. On assembly your mind has got an excess capacity to be able to start worrying about things. The absentee-ism in the factory is enormous. And the largest part of it, according to company statistics, comes from the assembly side, rather than the machine side. You read in the newspapers about obstreperous track workers going out on strike. This is all due to these pressures. To hit something with a hammer or to be disruptive is like a safety valve. It is just like a child who is put in a playpen and is confined. He suddenly starts to throw his teddy bear or his toy bricks around. And this is what happens with adults. They rebel against the environment they find themselves in. It is done as an outlet. It is not done in a malicious, bad way. It is difficult to try and explain it if you haven't really worked in it.

You get people who become very short-tempered. They feel that everyone is closing in on them. It makes a person very tense and nervous in the way he reacts. For instance, you can watch young people come into the factory and they are great people. They are stable. They are happy-go-lucky. They could not care less. They laugh, they joke; yet within two or three years they become a person who you can hardly speak to. It is not uncommon for people to say it is like going to prison for eight hours a day, being shut up and tied to a particular operation.

I have quite a bit to do with apprentices. They get these depressions. They seem to have more home problems than we did as children. With that pressure, along with the boredom, along with the work pressure, we are getting people dropping out at a high rate. Young people just do not want to carry on with the job. They say to themselves 'I cannot stand this any longer' and they just get out. But you find that even the ones who stick it out for four or five years are on some sort of tablet or another by the time they come out of their training. I do not know the reason for this, but it has become apparent over the last ten years or so that everyone has to survive on tablets.

At the beginning of the recession, to try and retain labour we slowed the tracks down. But obviously with the economic climate, we had to have redundancies in the end. Whereas British Leyland actually closed the whole factory down and got rid of the biggest bulk of labour, and then started up again, Massey Ferguson are doing it a different way. We retained the labour so we had a flow of production at a certain level, then we brought in the new techniques and we are now in the phase of getting rid of labour. And so we have an extra pressure. The people who have had to go through retraining and adapting to the new systems are now facing the pressure of have they got a job or haven't they got a job.

They bring in new technology in the pretence that it is a lot healthier to use these new systems. And to a degree this has proved true in two areas in welding. The robotic arm does relieve men from some dangerous work. But then you come into a deeper philosophy. As well as robotic arms we have also got data gathering systems, which involve visual display units, centralized computers and light pens. From the early fifties to the early seventies there was always a large back-up force to the machine shop and the assembly line, progress chasers, inspectors, clerks, material handlers and labourers. All of them were involved in getting parts to specific places at specific times. You can use 15,000 types of bolt or 15,000 types of washer in one production run lasting only ten hours. So that stuff has got repeatedly to be at the same place at the same time. Now under the new system all those people have gone, because the operator breaks the light signal every time he picks something up, and that is automatically counted by the computer, which then tells the main stores when the next batch needs to go out. In time we will not even need a truck driver to do the delivery because the truck will be guided by magnetic tape.

It has removed the personal contact that a chappie had. When someone was delivering things to him, or coming to check how much he had got, even if he only said 'Hullo, Bill' it was a break. That has been removed. The man is working virtually in isolation. The only thing he can talk to is a blessed machine or a gadget of some sort. Although the process has a built-in allowance for fatigue time, it does not actually build in an allowance for a man feeling sick or suddenly thinking 'Oh, God, I forgot to tell my wife something.' We have not got it as yet, but it will come to a situation where there is robot, human, robot, human, all the way down the track. The only thing a man can talk to is the ruddy robot on either side of him, but that is also pacing him. You have to go at the speed the robot is set at to produce the part. And you have also got to handle the nervous tension this produces. Also there is a built-in discipline. The man is monitored from the moment he goes on to the job to the minute he comes off, and there is a hell of a pressure.

It is not just happening on the manual side of the factory, it is also happening on the clerical side, with word-processing, electronic mailing and the systems X telephone. If for instance I was a typist and now I had become a word-processor, it signs me on with a date stamp automatically. If I am on a VDU I have to give it my personal code before I can do the functions I am meant to do. Now if those keys have not moved for ten minutes or quarter of an hour, it also times that delay. The individual is being timed and paced by the machine.

In the past, in car factories, tractor factories and other high-volume manufacturers, there used to be an intense number of human beings. There were large numbers of people all working together. Now you are one off. Whereas you were in a position to say to your mate 'Well, I don't feel very well', and he would help you out by doing a little bit extra, now there is no one to help. In the old days, on any main track if you got behind because you had got a faulty component, so you were breaking into the next station, people would pitch in and help you finish the operation. But with the new production methods that is impossible, because the next person to you could be so far away that you would have to go through two robotic stations. Now that damn thing would not help you, because it is only programmed to do its precise function.

And this is why you are getting people saying 'To hell with it, I have had enough. I want to get out.' They are taking their redundancy. We, from a trade union point of view, can say 'You are wrong. You should not sell a job', but they say to you quite honestly 'Who wants to come into this type of thing?' All that contributes to your health. The person who came out of the old type of production now finds himself in the new production and cannot take that pressure. A lot of people now in most working environments spend a lot of time on the sick. The bloke thinks 'I can't take any more. I've got to get out.' So he has a bad back. He's either suffering from headaches, he's suffering from blood pressure, or from some sort of nervous indisposition, and he utilizes that. There is nobody now that does not spend some time on the sick. It is a laughing joke within the staff areas. They have rotas for whose turn it is next. People cannot stand the strain of the new production.

From a union point of view you think 'Okay, reduce the working week.' But of course the company want to reduce the amount of money you earn in that reduced working week. So that again brings another pressure. If you can't afford to pay the mortgage, you are living under that sort of stress. It is not true to say that all the pressures are built just within the factory. A chappie is living in the same world as everybody else, and he has got excess pressure from outside. Now if he's got bad housing or a wife who is ill because of her job – she is probably in a clerical division somewhere, and she is coming under pressure, and she is getting on his nerves and he is getting on her nerves. He has got to work with that pressure already built into him. There is no way that someone can't be ill. It is impossible. The system has not been designed to give any sort of relief.

In the last couple of years the union has become more and more aware of the problem. But they still do not see it as a major issue. The major problem for them has always been wages and conditions. But that is a bit of a farce, because 'conditions' to them are toilets, time off from the job, clean overalls and extractor fans. They have not moved forward to understand that people need a different type of protection. There are people becoming more aware of it. For instance when VDUs began to appear, the main thing we used to look at was seating and lighting, and providing we had some kind of agreement that an oculist looked at people's eyes on a six-monthly basis, we were really quite happy with that. But it is becoming very, very apparent that it is no longer sufficient. We are in a terrible position with people breaking down, having nervous complaints, finishing up in the nuthouse at Warwick, by being tied to these new types of systems, particularly VDUs. The person is tied to a terminal, and the skill has been taken out of compiling a letter. She feels she has become part and parcel of the machine, and she is no more than a robot operating it. They just can't settle. They just can't live. Whereas before in a typing pool, or as a secretary, they were able to move, even if it was only across the office, there is none of that now. It all goes on floppy discs or into a computer terminal. They feel frustrated, they feel they are inadequate. They can't even turn round and have a chat. In the areas which used to be occupied by thirty or forty girls, there are now only two. They are also being timed by the machine. And all that puts a hell of a pressure on. They are tying people down so hard, it is just becoming drudgery to go to work.

On the technical side, where I work, we get different pressures. We have to put up with computer-aided design. Where a draughtsman used to be able to take pride in designing and drawing something up, he now sits in front of a TV screen and puts the design pattern on to it and it is done electronically. It is then transmitted electronically to a computer on the manufacturing side where the machines which are going to make the component are programmed. But nobody now is getting any personal achievement out of constructing these parts. Everybody's work is being de-skilled. A person has no longer got personal contact with the design of anything. At one time, before you could even design a nut and bolt, you had got to converse with a lot of other people who were also involved in the design of the same tractor. Today you are given a project by the computer to design a part. Yet you do not know where the part is going or even the overall look of the tractor you are involved in designing. There is no pride. Now you are writing this book. If, for instance, a computer had said to you: you will interview a Mr Gough and that it is the end of it, you do not know what the overall content of the book is going to be – what satisfaction would you get out of that? It is the same when you are designing a tractor, or a car. Or even a bomb. Unless you have got personal contact throughout the whole project, the thing suppresses the individual. I think all this affects people's health. They are taking away the human contact.

The other thing that happens is that you can now design what we call world cars, world tractors. You are probably designing the steering wheel here in England, but the actual wheels are being designed in Germany, and you have no overall picture of what the final track looks like. It is a lonely task.

We are finding that because of world slumps, whereas before we used to design and make a model which would last for eight to ten years, we are now finding that we have to update our models every twelve to eighteen months; so that pressure which used to come in surges, say every eight years, is now with you every eighteen months, so you are never really out of it. And a lot of people within Massey Ferguson, not only myself, are finding that their health is suffering as a result. Heart attacks or blood pressure problems are now so common I hardly know of anybody in my own environment that is not taking tablets of some sort, for that type of ailment. The other thing that is becoming very apparent is nervous complaints and also headaches. I would say probably seven in ten people suffer from that type of problem during the course of the year, and in some cases it is a continual suffering. But there is no one looking at why this is happening. No one is interested. Even local GPs just seem to want to write up a prescription for tablets and put it down to the kind of environment we live in.

My own problem started a number of years ago. I am married with six children, and everything in the world was smashing. I had no money worries or anything like that, because I had a reasonable job. But I used to work long hours, through choice, I suppose, and also to keep my earnings up. I worked for Triumph motorcycles, which the family had a large stake in, although I worked on the manual side. When Triumph motorcycles went into liquidation ten years ago I went to Masseys. The company was in its heyday, but they realized they would have to change the models, so we had three hectic years. We used to work from 7.30 in the morning to 6 at night, on Saturday from 7.30 in the morning to 4 in the afternoon, and on Sunday from 8 a.m. to 3.30 p.m., and that went on for three years with the exception of my holidays. But I found that most of my strain came from being involved in the trade union movement inside the factory. At times, when new forms of production are being introduced, the union side of the factory becomes very restless, which makes a lot more work. It means new agreements, piece-work timings, arguing whose job it is across demarcation lines. You do not get a minute to breathe within a day, you work eight hours solid, and you have your dinner walking round with a sandwich in your hand.

That was six years ago. At the end of that period, along with being out four or five nights a week at various meetings, I found I was putting on weight because of calling in for a pint on the way home. I was eating the wrong sort of food, and I was beginning to get very short of breath and feeling very tired. I didn't take a lot of notice when my wife said I better slow up a little. Then one New Year's Eve we went out for a meal and I collapsed on the way back. When they got me to hospital they found I had had a mild heart attack. From then on they decided to give me tablets and keep their eye on me. The tablets nearly drove me mad. I felt sick. I was nauseated all the time. But they persevered and got me on to some others, and I went back to work and felt quite happy.

Back at work, I got back into the same game. I found that I was taking on more and more work within the union. I felt quite well and so I thought I would let the tablets drop. That was because I always had a dislike of tablets. And lo and behold I got a thrombosis in my leg. I went round at work asking what it was like to have a pulled muscle in the back of my leg. And I thought that was what I had done. That went on for about two days. Then on Sunday morning when I was kneeling down in church I went to get up and the pain was that bad it made me cry. They took me down to the casualty department and before I realized it I was in intensive care. And the treatment was very good. They got me right again and I went back to work. About this time we were beginning to understand what the introduction of new technology meant. My trade union work intensified. As an individual I believe the only way to change things is to get involved in them. And then eighteen months ago I had another heart attack. It was my own fault – I was warned about it. My doctor was an absolute angel. He says I am a workaholic. He has begged and pleaded of me to take things easy, to settle down, drop out. But I am not that kind of individual.

Pension management: Ethel Fraser

They have put up a new bus shelter and some boys were trying to pull it down. It's shocking. And if you say anything they give you bad language. But I think this way: 'Poor lads, they have no money in their pockets. They are not working. What *she* is doing is wrong.'

Mrs Thatcher is coming to Sheffield next week. They are going to have to take all the buses off because of the crowds going to the protest march. I would love to go and tell her. Ask her how she would like to live on £33 a week, and pay £1.12 in rates. You see, they stop my rent before I get supplementary, but I still have to pay the rates. And I have worked all my life.

I worked at different places. First off, I worked at Wells on Charlotte Road. Then I worked in the market, and then I went to Sutherlands until I retired. I was a cook at Wilkinsons. At the market I cleaned the offices upstairs. At Sutherlands we made potted meat and other cooked meats.

I have three sons and a daughter in Australia. I didn't work when the children were small. But they used to go to school across the road from where I worked at the market. I used to go at six o'clock in the morning while nine. And then half past five at night while half past eight. On Saturday mornings it was six while twelve. It was hard work. I used to have to get the bus there and back, twice a day.

It didn't seem to affect my health at the time. I was all right. I hardly saw a doctor until I finished work. Then it seemed to all pile up together. I don't know why it was. Mind you, I worked hard. With mopping, and buffing up and sweeping, I used to go round one office four times. And then I had to get the coal bucket up. It was a lot. This lady that we worked for, she would take you off one floor on to another floor. You would perhaps be on two floors mopping. I worked so hard, I really did. When I worked at Sutherlands I was on shifts morning and afternoons, but I can't say I really felt tired.

I don't know how it has come about that I have been ill like this. First I had gland trouble. That was five years ago. And then I had a cyst on my pituitary gland. I have seen plenty of hospitals really. I feel fine now. I take the tablets. But these things come to test you, don't they? It was such a nuisance having to keep going into hospital. They told me it was my glands. I have to have thyroxin, two in the morning, all my life. Then I take two steroids three times a day. Then I have to take one tablet three times a day for my pituitary gland.

I'll tell you how the gland trouble originated. My daughter came from Australia. She said 'You don't look well.' I said 'I'm all right.' But she told the doctor, and the doctor sent me to hospital. At the hospital they tested me for everything, everything. It put me about, that. They said it was the glands and gave me tablets. I went to the doctor last week about it, so I am hoping to God everything is going to be all right. I have been in hospital three or four times. For the pituitary gland I had radium treatment. The doctor said he was positive he could cure it. I had a scan on it recently, and the doctor says it is very satisfactory, so I am keeping my fingers crossed.

Sometimes you worry. Sometimes I worry. I think 'What is really wrong?' When I went to hospital last week the doctor said 'What are you worrying over?' But you do. Somebody was saying that gland trouble can take your sight. And that is what really does worry me. Touch wood. I went to the optician and I said 'Is it affecting my sight?' He said 'Don't be silly, woman.' But, as I say, it has affected the left eye. But God is good, he will see us through, I am sure.

You work all your life, and then this comes to you. It makes you wonder, doesn't it? I have a sister. She is eighty this year. She worked until she was seventy-four. Yet she has been ill all the time since she retired. And she has not been able to go nowhere. She has water trouble which blows her out. She can't walk. She can't do much for herself, and yet she worked until she was seventy-four.

I have had the fire off all morning. I only put it on when you came. Don't worry, I have to put it on some time or it gets cool. You are frightened to have it on. You are frightened of the bills coming in. I have central heating, but I have never had it on. I daren't have my central heating on because I would never be able to meet the bill. When it was really cold, my son kept saying 'Mum, put that fire on', but you can't afford to. My sons can't afford to give me it. They have problems of their own. They have big bills. They have been on strike. At work they have been on one day a week. They can't afford to help me. You can't do much with £33 a week, can you? I always give my youngest son £8 every week to cover the gas and the electric. He saves it. And then when the bills come in he just takes them. I don't have to do anything about it. I get two stamps for my television licence every week. But she is doing to us that we will not be able to live.

There is a pensioner across the road. She is the same. She has her son living with her. And she does not put money away for bills. She takes it out of her son's money when he gets his. He gets two weeks at a time. So this weekend she has nothing, because he got his money last weekend. Now she would not dream of putting one week away. If I get two weeks' pension, I don't touch it. I put it away and then I bring it out as if I had been to the post office.

It takes some doing, managing. Sometimes you have not got enough to last you until Tuesday, and sometimes you might have a few coppers left over. But you are ready for Tuesday coming. I think you have a right to enjoy your retirement. But she is taking it off us. If I could get a pound, or two pounds of rotten, real rotten tomatoes I would put them in her face, whatever they did to me. Because she is horrid, so horrid. She is a horrible woman.

My son, he has got two kiddies. One, Samantha, won't stay to school dinners. She is a very poor eater. But Debbie does stay to dinner. Did it used to be 5p a week? Now it is £2 odd a week.

What she is doing to these young boys is audacious. That young fellow I was talking about, my neighbour's son, he has been unemployed for a long, long time – so long I can't remember what work he did, to tell you the truth.

Look what they've done. They've got these boys on these schemes working for £23 a week. My nephew's son is on it. He has to pay four bus fares every day. It is just cheap labour for them. There are some young fellows in their forties who know they have not got a chance in hell of getting another job. Can you blame people doing extra jobs while they are on the dole? I know it is wrong, but I don't blame them. Good luck to them.

At one time you could take a £5 note and get nearly two bags full of things. Now you can't get a bag full with the same amount of money. It is the same with clothes. You can't buy clothes, because you have not got the money. My youngest son and his wife bought me a dress the other week. It is not fair to be taking it off them. But what can you do? You have no money.

When you go out you have to study. You see something and you have to ask 'Can I afford it?' So you don't buy it. I know that there are many, many pensioners like me, they see many a thing and you think 'Oh, I would enjoy that', but then you think 'I can't afford it.' And you don't buy it. Nowadays for a pound you can probably get two things.

We have a good council here, but when I came out of hospital they said I could have a home help for a few weeks, and then a lady came and said I would have to pay. I said I couldn't afford it, so she said 'I will see what I can do.' Well, they sent one on a Wednesday afternoon and then I never saw her again for another six weeks. When she came again, I said 'Tell them not to bother, love, I am managing. I have had to manage for five weeks and so I might as well manage.' That's what hurts people. They come once, then they come weeks later. Well, that is no good to us.

When I came out of hospital they put me on a diet, and they gave me a medical certificate for social security. I didn't want to go, and I told the doctor I would rather not go. But he said 'Look, Mrs Fraser, you can't afford this diet.' It was white meat and all things like that. He says 'Will you promise me you will go? Just give them the certificate.' So I went. The woman at the social security interrogated me, in effect. Then she said, and this is true, 'Well, we can allow you ten pence.' I said 'Ten pence! I have got three little tomatoes in my bag and these cost me fifteen pence.' I said 'I think it is terrible you send a book out for ten pence.' She said 'We send a book out for five pence.' So I said 'You know what you can do with your ten pence, don't you?'

The diet was to get the weight off. There was white fish and white meat, chicken, rabbit and all things like that. When I told my son, he said 'Mother, don't worry. Don't go no more. We will see to you.' Well, they were working full-time then and they used to bring fish and meat for me. But when you think you have paid all your tax all those years and they say 'We can give you ten pence', that's cruel.

My three sons, they all brought me things. With gland trouble, you keep putting weight on. It is not because you eat a lot. The glands put it on for you. I do try to lose weight. I just cook potatoes. If I do have chips, I will just have about half a dozen. And I will have some stew meat and that. My youngest son, he brings me things perhaps two or three times a week. And every Sunday in the three years he has been married, he has brought me my Sunday dinner. I have got three good sons. I can go any time I like and stop. Or they say 'Come up, Mum, to us. It will save you gas.'

I'm lucky, because my sons bring me meat. I could not afford to buy it. It is much too dear. I eat properly. But there are many, many pensioners who don't. Now my neighbour – you can go over there and she has not had anything all day. And now she has got something coming on her skin. I don't know whether it is an abscess or what. And she is always cold. In the hottest day of summer she is frozen. But she will not go and see to herself. She can go all day without having a meal. She says she is not hungry, but it is because she can't really afford to buy anything. Now I went in this morning and all she had had was a cup of tea and a biscuit. I can't go without my food. I am all right. I have a hot meal every day, even if it is a drop of hash. Or potatoes and greens. I always have something. Tea, I am not bothered. I might just have a little scone or a cup of tea. But I do like my dinner. I love my dinner. I think that puts you on for the day, if you have a good meal. There are times when I have not had any meat, and I have done some carrots and onions and potatoes and I have had them. If they would only give us a little bit more to live on it would help a bit. If she would only give us three or four pounds a week more, that is what I would like to see.

I hope to God she never gets in again. People are just absolutely fed up with her. She keeps making them redundant. They always keep talking about they are going to merge this factory and that one. They are talking about Tinsley Park now. That is English Steel. They are going to make I don't know how many redundant there. My sons work at English Steel, but at the River Don Works. At least the two older ones do. The younger one works for the council. But the other two – Billy, he's forty-three, and Malcolm – they've worked there since they left school.

My husband – he was a casting steel crane driver – he was sure of a job. He could go to work and come home. Go to work and come home. Whereas now, my sons and thousands of lads like them do not know from one day to the next whether they will have work. They can be in work one day and out the next. My husband had a true job. There was no such thing as redundancies and short-time working as there is today. He did not get the money they gain today, but it was a permanent job. My two sons don't believe in striking, because they say you are in the same position at the end as what you were at the beginning. You have no money. But the other week they had to come out, and all he drew was £13 for his wife and two kids. His rent is £24 something.

I think it is harder work now than it was in my husband's time. My eldest son is a casting crane driver too, while my middle son, he is a melter. Melters melt the steel. They are in front of the furnaces all the time. His is a real hard job. My eldest son can do three castings in one go. That is putting steel into moulds. My husband was tired when he came home, but my sons seem ever so tired when they come home. I think they have to do more. They are rushing more. They have to do more productivity, they call it bonus. It is the bonus which makes the wages up. Without any bonus the wages are nothing.

But still we get by, don't we? We don't have to be maundy. I am lucky in having my family, but there is still loneliness. When it is dark nights, you shut your door at four o'clock. You lock it. You are in all night on your own. It is very lonely. But as I say, I am very lucky. But there are some poor old souls who have not got nobody.

My mother died when I was sixteen, but my older brother was a steeple-jack and he used to buy us things. He used to take us to buy clothes and shoes. Those were poor days. But today is worse. In those days a neighbour was a neighbour, but you can't say that now. Where I lived before, you used to go out of your door and there was a wall. We would be sat out there at two and three in the morning with cups of coffee. Those days were a lot different to what they are now. People were poor, but there were comforts. There was more happiness and more laughter.

I have seven grand-daughters and one grandson. I want them to be happy. I want them to get on. But I do not know where the next generation will be. I do not know where the future will be.

Spare part: George Taylor

I am in a state of limbo. I am sixty-two. Two years ago the firm closed itself down in a fit of pique and moved off. People younger than me are in a bit of a plight, but at least in the foreseeable future they might get a job. There is still part of life for them to live. But I can't offer my services to an employer, because even if he likes my experience, he knows that I would only have three years to go.

It is the situation of being an outcast. We often said 'It'll be all right when we get retired. We like travelling that much, we can go on these nice cheap holidays.' But we can't. We always looked forward to the idea we could go on package holidays. I don't mean every week, but two or three trips during the summer. We thought we could afford those things. To go on cheap trips, it would not be too much out of the way. All right, it is true, we can have a walk round the park and go locally. If the weather gets nice, we can both please ourselves and go off. It is a wonderful feeling not having to work after a lifetime of work, but the means to enjoy it is not there.

I have to face the fact that my income is not going to get any more, but I do not have the benefits which retirement status would bring. We are preferred against. Who knows I might not be one of those who get to sixty-five. I am reasonably healthy, but I have seen all too many of my colleagues struck down before they even got to my age. People who died before they were sixty. It could be argued that it was the type of work they were doing. Working in a factory day after day after day. The horrible, monotonous, literal grind of standing there. Even standing there doing no work is work itself, predisposing you to varicose veins. You get all sorts of aching pains, which are probably due to working in cold, nasty conditions. When you stop work like me, you find you have to begin to use your legs again in a certain way.

And then there are bronchial ailments. My work was as a tool and cutter grinder. You do regrinding of tools to very fine limits. Whether they have got a fan operating or not, you get a certain amount of grinding dust on your chest.

When I first went to the factory there were 200 workers, but by their efficiency methods and their so-called rationalization, bringing in computer-controlled machines, they managed to halve that. Closing the factory was a shabby thing to do. We were on strike about a pay claim. Then they said 'If you don't come back we are going to chop a third of you.' So we resisted that. And then they said 'And don't suppose you are going to get redundancy payments if you are on strike.' Then they sent out our redundancy notices. But we continued to picket the place as if we were still on strike. In the end they called in ACAS, and we never got real redundancy, just a portion of it which was called 'compensation'.

I had worked there for seven and a half years. Before, I also did turning and milling. I have worked on machine tools all my life. I did not enjoy my work. If you were born like me in the twenties and were leaving school in the depression of the thirties, it was something to have got a job, *a* job. It is by no means the job I would have chosen. My father was a turner, and he should have done anything he could to keep me away from the engineering industry. Better to have been a plumber, painter, decorator, baker – I won't say butcher – or candlestick maker. I would have preferred something that was more artistic in its nature. There is no more horrible and monotonous job in the world than manufacturing industry. I don't just mean engineering. Whether it is pharmacy, or food manufacture, they are all soul-destroying jobs, particularly if you are on a production line. Like these fellows at British

Leyland, who I have a lot of sympathy with. They are being told, *told*, mind you, that they cannot have three minutes to wash their hands. This is the kind of thing we have to put up with all our lives.

I meet people who are still working, and I say to myself 'I couldn't do that now.' I couldn't do it. My wife looks for a job for me in the paper as a matter of course, but I say 'I hope you have not found me a job!' I couldn't go and work in a factory now. The mental adaptation to it is now lost. I couldn't tell my legs 'Never mind, you are going to have a break soon.' My body would not stand for it.

For two years I have enjoyed the benefit of getting up every day and saying 'I have not got much going for me, but today is my *own*.' That is the secret. That is what keeps me going. I can literally do what I like within a given framework. If I want to walk round the park, as I did yesterday, with my wife, I can do. If we want to go into town, we can. We can have a cup of coffee, look round the shops, go into a museum. I like the freedom to do what I want to and I could no more go back into that factory now than fly. The mind would not let the body do it any more.

Unemployment does sap at the ego which tells you that you are a useful part of the community. Works gives an identity to a person. But to me all factory workers have made themselves into a kind of robot that happens to speak. But to me that is not living. I am doing more living now than I was at that factory. My mind has got things to feed on and enjoy. Even if it is only thinking in the park. When you are stood at a machine, that machine is capturing all your thoughts. It even stops thought. I tried to say to myself 'Well, this job is so monotonous, why don't I manipulate the skill part with my hands and reserve my mind for thinking about what I want to think about?' But I found that was a very dangerous thing to do. Because most of your mind is interested in the things that are interesting and you are having to fasten the other part on to the monotonous things, you could find yourself very grievously injured. A slight slip could mean the loss of fingers or eyesight. Or you could find yourself ravelled up in the machinery in a terrible way.

I had been led to believe that we were doing a marvellous job for the country. I was among people who called themselves engineers and had been told they were the cream of the working class. I don't like 'cream' as a description. But if you were in manufacturing, especially during the war years, that was what you were told. You felt you would be looked after. That as you came to the end of your working life, there would be earlier retirement to look forward to and a shorter working week. When I first started work at the age of fourteen, we worked a forty-seven-hour week. That was five days and a Saturday morning. What happened to the mooted thirty-five-hour week? Then as automation came on and later computerization, we talked about a twenty-five-hour week, but we never did get lower than forty. And in practice, with overtime, we were still working forty-seven hours when it suited the employers.

I have resisted overtime all my life. It is an evil. Going back to my apprentice days, I used to think 'What is the point of going to work extra time to put money in your pocket which then deprives you of the time to enjoy that money?' But the crunch was that even if you were against overtime, if your wife said we need to pay this bill or that bill you were more or less obliged to go along with the system. It was also a case of the iron fist in the velvet glove. Technically overtime is not compulsory, but if you refuse to do it too many times they will get rid of you. I once went for a job and they said 'By the way, we expect you to work ten or fifteen hours extra.' And when I said 'I don't want to work overtime', they looked at me as if there was something really wrong with me. It is far better, the employers reason, if you have already got somebody who you are paying stamps for, to load him up with extra work when it comes in, and reduce it when there is less work, than to employ extra workers and have all those costs exaggerated. Yet people are prepared to put up with this. Mad keen trade union fellows have said to me 'It is something for us.' I have said 'It isn't. You are digging your own grave, ruining your own health, surely.'

Overtime ruins people's health. I have seen people brought down by overtime. I have seen grey putty-like complexions and hacking coughs. And a mental attitude. You can see a bowing of their heads and a blinkered look. It shows itself in strikes. At this last firm, we were on various strikes, long strikes, and I found that even when people were invited to sit-in at the factory, they couldn't enjoy it. They would say 'Oh, I am bored.' They were ready for getting up and giving in. Because they literally did not know what to do with themselves. I believe that just as people in the upper brackets have their leisure, their golf, all people have this will, this need, for something else to sustain the human spirit.

I have stood at my machine and worked it out for myself. There are 168 hours in a week. A third of them are taken up sleeping, if you are going to do right by yourself. You can take another piece off for ablutions, travelling back and forth to work, your washing off and getting your breakfast at one end and your tea at the other. That brings it up to something like ten. So then you have not got much left of your twenty-four hours. I remember the words of William Morris, who said he refused to accept that some people were born to have everything done for them and live a life of luxury, fed by other people who are pre-destined to have a yoke put round their neck and put to work. I think his words are as true today as they were then.

Shifts are another obnoxious thing. Sometimes I have worked shifts, but I have tried to find jobs which did not involve shiftwork. Mornings are not so bad. The only thing is you have to get up at a fantastically early hour. They were from six until two. At least you had the afternoons free and then you started to get tired, so you couldn't stay out too late. The afternoon shift is the worst of the lot. It is two until ten. You get up in the morning, and you are waiting to go on at two, but you can't do anything with that time. You can't go anywhere, because you have got to come back. That feeling is like waiting to be shot. Nights is not too bad, ten until six next morning, but it is an unsocial thing. What does happen on nights is that all your digestive system is upset. If you go on nights once a fortnight or once every three weeks, your stomach has got to get used to the fact that you are not going to bed and that you are going to start feeding it stuff in the middle of the night. Two o'clock in the morning is the time when you are at your lowest ebb; all your powers, concentration, physical wellbeing drain away. I used to find this as regular as clockwork. You used to find that you had got it a little bit assimilated by the end of the week, when it was time to change over again. So this, over a period of time, plays havoc with you. I have known people develop very nasty ulcers spending their working life on shifts.

I am not a person who is dead against work. I always think what a nice thing it is to work at a job you would choose yourself. To work at something you would do anyway for a hobby, like decorating or photography. All the products I have worked on are of no value to me. Some of us in this city have worked on things that are mainly neither use nor ornament, particularly armaments. I have worked in armaments factories. All they are made for is to destroy people and maim them, and they are no good for anything else but that. There are some products, like agricultural tools, that are useful. Even a tatty thing like a shovel is a wonderful thing. You can put it in the earth, which will cause something to grow, which will create a bit of wealth. I would have liked to have been in the type of work which produces an attractive result, even if it is only a service. I always think that those who are in service industries are a lot better off than those who have to produce a product. When you are producing a product you have always got someone breathing down your neck, saying you are not doing it fast enough or accurate enough.

Now I feel in limboland. Healthwise there is this thing about the human spirit. We are gregarious people. We like to belong to a little outfit, even if it is the few that you sit with at the pub – I used to enjoy a drop of beer, but I don't go now, not with beer at more than 50p a pint. You like to belong to a little group. You don't like being excluded from it. If you go to work you get that gregariousness. I have known me come to work and think 'I don't want to come here this morning. I didn't want to come here yesterday. I shan't tomorrow either.' And then I have thought 'But there is one thing to it. I am meeting a cross-section of people every day, enjoying their company, having a laugh and joke with them, helping each other with general tasks.' You miss the benefit of being together. You miss that. You feel like a spare part.

I was enjoying fairly good health until just after I got made redundant. I started to do basic do-it-yourself work on the house, which involved climbing ladders. Instead of using safety shoes, I put ordinary ones on and the aluminium rung pressed deep into my instep. I didn't think much about it at the time. Then I had a rather nasty happening. My brother, who lived across the road, had recently retired. And retirement affected him in a totally different way to me. He went right down without his work, and he died. I found him just on a social visit. In fact I was taking him an ice cream. I had all the worry of sorting out the arrangements and the cremation. Then I was very hurt by the way in which my other brother and myself were disinherited in a family which was very close and believed in fairness and sharing. My nerves were shot to pieces. I found that I was limping really badly, and it went to my knee. I went to the doctor and had an X-ray. It turned out that a ridge of bone had grown on the underside of my foot, but the doctor said the pain of it had been induced by my low mental state. You can't cheat on your body. The doctor said that there was nothing he could do, but that I should try to keep a semi-cheerful mental state. And it has got progressively better.

I am also on blood pressure tablets. I am taking part in a trial on the effectiveness of treating it with medication. My blood pressure was relatively high. The doctor said it was nothing to worry about, and it has been brought down by the tablets. All right, I have the aches and pains one expects in later life, but I think I am in quite good health. I asked the doctor 'Am I a fairly good physical specimen? I would like to know.' He said 'Considering your age, both your mental attitude and your physical state is very good.'

I also asked another doctor at the surgery. He said 'I would not kid you. I am not saying you are top-class, but considering the job you have had and considering what you have had to put up with and what has recently happened to you, I think that you are well above average, quite good.'

Make no mistake, I enjoy my life in the limited way it is. But I think 'What have I done to deserve this?' You shouldn't have to think like this, but often when we are in town and see some poor devil without any legs, or someone who is blind, we say to each other 'You forget how lucky you are to have the functions you have got, to be able to see things, to hear things, touch things, be able to walk, use your limbs.' But still I say you shouldn't have to live your life saying how lucky you are compared to some people. You shouldn't be having to say 'Oh, aren't I lucky at the side of other people.' You should be taking things for granted in that sense. Good health should be a right.

Half not well: Vera Mitchell

My name is Vera Mitchell. I am forty-three, but do not feel any particular age. I live in a council flat in Harlesden on the corner of two busy roads. Across the road there is Willesden Junction, and up the road there is a chemical storage plant. I live with my two daughters. Sarah, who is nineteen, is leaving to work abroad for the summer. It's a big step for her, but she's fed up with the violence and dead-end feeling of Harlesden. Kim is three, bright and very active. Since a baby, she has had a dietary condition which means chronic diarrhoea. Until recently I have been changing and cleaning her up seven or eight times a day, as well as controlling her diet. Doing it *with* her, rather than *to* her, takes a lot of time and patience.

Although I have great moments of contentment and wellbeing, I don't think I will ever be well. That's not me being self-pitying. It's a fact. I have phlebitis caused by recurring clots. Once I had a clot in my lung, and I have also had them in my leg. This thrombosis is very painful. I also have a kind of arthritis with fusing in my joints and spine. But I have another problem, too. The label that can be put on it is a kind of agoraphobia. It is to do with difficulty getting out of the house, something a lot of women experience. It's a physical thing. You get into a panic. You feel sick at the thought of going out of the door. Three years ago I did not get out of this flat for three months.

None of my friends knew; you can hide it very successfully. You can always say 'While you are passing, can you pop in the bread?' or 'Listen, on the way home from school can you get in the supper?'

Some days I cannot get out of my bedroom. I cannot face the responsibilities of running the day. I get very muddled, confused, even about how to make a cup of tea. Simple actions, like dealing with the kettle, become very complicated. With me the reason for it is I can't turn off. You walk around Harlesden and you see grey pinched faces. And you go through the motions: 'How are you?', 'Very well, thank you' – and you know they are not. And you've got to make a snap decision; do I reach out further? It takes me two or three hours to do half an hour's shopping. Other people's pain becomes your pain. I cannot bear the anger in me of what is around us. I want to change it. I want to alter it.

When agoraphobia becomes severe it is an individual thing, but many women experience it to some degree. I think that especially women on a low income, like me, come to accept that the outside world is not meant to be in your sphere of influence. It is not your right, you lose the confidence. Your family gets sick. You have to stay in and nurse them. Then it becomes difficult to have space for yourself. You get out of practice in going out.

I don't think that agoraphobia and depression are separate – you can think they are separate. Like today, I had planned to go to friends to do this interview, but I couldn't get out. Now I wasn't feeling overtly depressed. Depression is not just having your head in your hands and feeling sorry for yourself. A depressed state slows you down. You feel uninteresting, and dull. It seems as if you are surrounded by a wall. On extreme days I feel as if I am viewing people through the end of a long, dark tunnel. You wake up with your heart literally pounding. And you see all your failures going through your head, flash, flash, flash. You feel you can't connect with other people. You want a lot of loving, but you won't let people near you. You are screaming inside yourself 'Love me, touch me with words, touch me with feelings.' But you are just solid. There is part of you that feels very vulnerable, like a child, and yet there is a part of you looking at yourself, knowing exactly what you are doing.

It is not simple to describe the pressure that pushed me into depression. A long time on a low income, bad housing, being surrounded by people in similar situations, not being mobile. But it is more than that. The guilt is terrible. *You* feel the failure. Considering I've got some sense of what is causing my depression, it is surprising that it still hits me so hard. It is quite a stark thing that I experience, but most of the women round here are depressed in some form, whether it is to do with relationships within the home, the relationship of home and work, or with lack of work. Isolation is another factor, especially in high-rise flats. I have lived in both, and the streets with back fences were much more friendly. You will be with a group of women, and through dialogue common factors will come out. The thing of not being able to get up in the morning. That feeling of being in a pub and thinking 'What am I doing here?' That lack of sense of joy; that inability to share; that closing down; that sadness; that frustration. A very common thing that happens is being near to tears inside of yourself. Depression is a squashing down of yourself and what you can do.

A lot of my states are caused by a feeling of powerlessness. A feeling that you have not got the power to do anything about your immediate circumstances. We are all feeling it. More and more the little we have got is being taken away from us. We are not even able to defend what we have got, our jobs, our ability to keep our homes together, our ability to feed our kids successfully. In the sixties it was not quite so stark. You had the ability to save up for a washing machine. You had your housing repairs done, with a bit of a struggle, but you got them done. Now it's different. I think unemployment hits women very, very hard. Not just because they lose their jobs first – in Park Royal the part-time jobs were the first thing that went – but also you are carrying people who are feeling the depression of unemployment. Our houses are running down again now, too. It is not just the obvious thing of the damp, which gives you cold after cold until you are weakened into bronchitis. It is also the demoralization. You feel ashamed that your house smells of mould. Not having any money is very grinding, very putting down. But it is not an obvious one. It is not about not being able to provide shoes for your kids. Daily, daily, daily you lose the worth of yourself.

Physical illness, or physical whatever you want to call it, is so bound up with yourself and the way you are dealing with things. You have no sooner finished paying one bill than another is through the door. You do not go round with it in the front of your head all the time, but it is there. To eat well can be cheap, but you have to have the knowledge and the confidence to do it. There are so many pressures on you that you are not providing the basics, it is a terrible thing to carry around. People's only alternative is to earn a bit of money on the side of their supp. ben., but that means breaking the law, which is another hidden pressure. We are continually being drained by having to fight in the only areas that are available to us. Where do you go? You shout your mouth off at whatever place is getting at you the worst. You go up to the DHSS and holler through a glass panel at somebody. You demand a social worker to help you get your bills paid or whatever it is, and with the DHSS, you are told you are a bad manager if you can't pay your bills. Your money is taken away from you, and you don't even have your own money to handle. What sort of worth have you got then? I know one young woman with two children. She has £15 a week coming in by the time her rent and electricity and gas is taken off. With two children. With £15 a week. And she is not alone. It is common.

Your desperation about your situation comes out as constant colds, and headaches, and hitting the kids, and not being able to express yourself through your sexuality. The illnesses which people do not acknowledge include depression, the aches and pains of the body, from arthritis or extreme tension, or menstruation problems that are never taken seriously, and a lot of gynaecological problems. Women particularly almost don't feel it is their right to be completely well. The quality of our lives is that we are in some pain or other. Pain is the common thing. Emotional or mental or physical or all together. It becomes compounded.

What does illness mean? Our level of 'being well' is wrong. Most people are half not well most of the time. The thing is that so many people are actually not aware of it. It is the way expectancies of what constitutes a healthy person are being lowered that I find so distressing. If we have a good year, or a good day, we think 'Wow!', but it should not be like that. What makes us sick is the environment we live in. Yet the frightening thing is that we are evolving a kind of tolerance to it. It is like moving from a quiet road to a noisy road. When you first move in you think 'Oh, hell, I am not going to sleep.' Gradually you start going to sleep, with that noise or not. But those decibels are still there. The quality of your sleep is not the same. You are unconsciously being damaged. But you accept. We accept the things that make us not well. A lot of what is harming us is deep down in our subconscious. The ultimate issue is the whole nuclear disarmament question. I see that as a health issue. It is there with us, with all of us, more and more. It is one of the reasons underlying the hopelessness and the depression most people feel.

If you bring to doctors what is causing your problems, they say it is an excuse, a get-out. There is an awful lot of blame put back on you. Doctors respond to the depression, headaches, backaches, bowel problems, and all our other not-very-wellness, by doling out drugs. I think even the best of doctors narrow themselves down to that. If a doctor begins to open himself up and realize what is causing it, I am sure he would feel so isolated that he would have to narrow himself down again to survive. I couldn't give figures, but a good majority of women and men round here are on tranquillizers, sleeping tablets or pain killers. An awful lot of women feel fobbed off. And I think addiction to those drugs is increasing, out of desperation. I don't think it is out of lack of awareness of what they do to you. I think drugs stop people fighting back, but then I think that the reasons why those people are taking the tablets also stop people fighting back. By the time you get to the doctor, the damage has already been done, as far as fighting back is concerned.

We are fodder. We feel that. I have always been politically active in the community, trying to change things, to make a better future for myself and my kids, and for everyone. It is hard. To change anything you have to start from the roots. So many times you can only change things on the surface. The things that make us sick are so removed from us. It is partly lack of money, partly the environment, partly the attitudes we encounter from officialdom, and partly the way we are divided from one another. I don't believe it can be changed through the ballot box. It's the structures. We live in a sick society. A crippled society. A society that is in a terrible muddle. A potentially brutal society. And it damages, it damages.

3 Conditions of our Lives

Before we did the interviews we set out to illustrate connections between people's lives and their health which have already been demonstrated in the research literature. We were looking for evidence of how eating well is difficult on a low income, of how children without playspace are vulnerable to accidents, of the hazards of work, of the damage unemployment does, as well as of the effects of isolation in the home, and of piece-work, shift-work and overtime. We wanted to show the connections between everyday life and health. But what emerges from people talking is a picture of that interconnectedness which is far more complex than we had imagined. The interviews graphically show the health-damaging consequences of environmental and work hazards, housing conditions and inadequate incomes. But we were taken aback by the emphasis most of the eight also put on loneliness, isolation, the meaninglessness of work, and power-lessness as causes of ill health in our society.

Dominant explanations

The class pattern of ill health is not a subject which gets a wide airing on television, in the newspapers or in schools. The government's reluctance in 1980 to publicize the contents of the Black Report,[1] which highlighted class inequalities in health, printing only 260 duplicated copies, indicates that it does not want to encourage us to dwell too deeply on the question of who gets ill and why.

Inside medical and social policy circles, however, the picture is a bit different. Class differences and the reasons for them are a topic of occasional discussion. With the rising cost of medicine, the policy-makers are concerned to find ways of reducing what they see as 'self-inflicted' illness. Although this book focuses on the contrast between the health of most people and that of the ten or fifteen per cent at the top of society, government policy-makers, sociologists and health education experts tend to look at the distribution of ill health in a different way. As they see it, most of us have reasonable health; we are all part of some vast middle class; but there is a hard core, a residual group, whose health is less good. The third of the population that is consigned by official statisticians to 'social class three' is ignored, and the problem is conceptualized in terms of the contrast between the responsible social class ones and twos and the irresponsible fours and fives.

The dominant explanation of the class pattern of ill health is that it is due to *behaviour* differences. Ones and twos take the advice doctors give them; they have the intelligence to know what is good for them and the willpower and self-control to resist health-damaging practices. They give up smoking, take up jogging, eat high-fibre diets and read about stress management in the Sunday papers. The four and fives are thick. They live from day to day, never thinking of their future decrepitude. They smoke, they drink, they live on crisps and fizzy pop. They are not interested in contraception. They are promiscuous. They ignore the advice of health professionals. They do not bother to go for antenatal care or to take their children to the clinic. The literature on this topic talks of the 'educationally resistant', of the problem of 'effective communication' and of the 'cycle of deprivation'. People persist in health-destructive behaviour, it is argued, because they have learned it as children and teach it to their children. On the dilapidated hard-to-let council estates and in the inner cities where nice people fear to tread, there is a culture of self-destruction. The task of the health professional is to crack it.

Another view

Socialists, and others who find that the notion that people's ill
health is their own fault sticks in their throats, have taken a
different view.[2] Their argument is in two parts. Firstly, they
point out that working-class people are iller because they are
more exposed to a health-damaging environment over which
they have little control. People who work in mines, factories or
laundries experience hazardous working conditions. At home
there is no way you can expect people to be healthy if they are
living in damp or overcrowded conditions. Of course working-
class kids are more likely to have accidents if there is nowhere
for them to play or if they are living in houses with paraffin stoves
because their mum can't afford the electric. Even air pollution,
which at first sight appears to affect us all, hurts the people who
live in the built-up city areas more than those who live in the leafy
suburbs. Pensioners are bound to die of hypothermia with
the rocketing cost of fuel. Hypothermia is a problem of class as
well as age. When has an eighty-year-old high court judge or
a lord ever been admitted to a casualty department blue with
cold?

Secondly, we counter the 'feckless at fault' argument by pointing out that even where people's ill health is linked with aspects
of their lives which at first sight appear to be under their control,
particularly diet, drinking and smoking, account must be taken
of the social pressures which drive people to smoke, drink, and
eat badly. With food it is partly money – most pensioners see
fresh fruit as a luxury beyond their means – partly time (cooking
wholefoods is seen to take time and energy, which are often at
a premium in households where the adults are working), and
partly because chips, cakes, sweets and chocolate temporarily
cheer us up. People who see hope for the future can enjoy
investing in a little self-denial now. But if you don't see any hope,
if the future seems grey, if you have no alternative sources of
enjoyment, like holidays, to look forward to, then comforting

yourself now makes sense. This is also true of cigarettes and alcohol. When there seems no way out of pressure at work, tension inside the family, money worries or fears about ill health, who does not turn to drinking or smoking?

Implicating society

The dominant explanation of the greater ill health of people at the bottom of society focuses on individual behaviour. Ill health is seen as a personal responsibility. Socialists have taken a different view, pointing to the way companies put profit before health both in terms of what is produced and the way it is produced. We argue that the logic of capitalism is that it doesn't matter if junk food, cigarettes, alcohol or weapons can damage us as long as they sell. And it doesn't matter, either, if workers in the factories or the people living near them are damaged by the way the product is made. The employers are interested in keeping the process as cheap as possible in order to make the most money, which means not spending on safety measures or slowing down production to a safe speed. We point out how, although it is sometimes possible to campaign for protective legislation, the state bows to the pressure of private capital in not enforcing stricter controls. The Health and Safety Inspectorate is short of money and lacks the muscle to control employers. Local councils underfund their environmental health departments, which could put much more pressure on landlords to improve rented property. We point to the evidence that unemployment damages our health. We argue that government policies on housing, pensions and other areas of welfare compound the health problems people face.

We have taken the areas where epidemiology and other research provide us with clear-cut evidence of the things which damage us and pointed to the way in which private capital and the state are implicated in the production of ill health. The interviews bear out this analysis. Andrew Tree's bitterness is not just towards his employers, who showed extreme disregard for the health and lives of their workers; it is also directed towards the Health and Safety Inspectorate, which overlooked the dangers of the use of BisCME in his factory for many years, and towards the government, which he sees as colluding with the chemical industry in not enforcing stricter controls. Les Bennett shows how a Labour council is responsible for thousands of properties which are so seriously dilapidated they are a danger to health. Shan Jagedo shows how, where there is little union resistance, as in the second factory she worked in, employers will exploit the extreme vulnerability of their workforce, exposing them to chemicals and machinery which are even more dangerous than in unionized factories. Vera Mitchell is angry with the council about its failure to take action on damp housing, and with the government for its failure to act on lead. Ethel Fraser links her neighbour's poor health with an inadequate diet and knows from her own experience how impossible it can be to eat what you need to be healthy on a low income. George Taylor and Les Bennett point out how difficult it is to give up smoking if you are under stress from bad housing, a low income or unemployment.

Feelings too

But what is striking about the interviews is that all eight describe the pressures on their health in a way which is more abstract and complex than the amalgam of environmental hazards, diet and stress highlighted by research.

Vera argues that it is not only that there is something in the mould that gets on your chest, but that the demoralization of living in damp housing in itself affects your health. It is not just that being on social security makes it harder to feed your kids well, but that constantly having to worry about meeting bills and rent arrears grinds you down. The point she is making is that it is the *being ground down* which makes you liable to illness,

particularly chronic conditions. Baden acknowledges the physical dangers of dermatitis, the strain of lifting heavy weights and
the hazards of welding, but his main point is that it is the
destruction of human contact and the monotony of work which
cause health problems in his factory, from heart attacks to headaches. Andrew Tree says that the workers' health is affected by
the worry of the possibility they may have cancer, as well as by
the cancer itself. Shan is very aware of the physical hazards of
the factory but also attributes some ill health to the pressure of
work and the competition between workers in her factory. She
also emphasizes the dangers to health of there being so little time
for relaxation, especially among women who both go out to work
and do housework. George insists that long hours and the monotony of work are as damaging to health as the specific hazards
of the factory, like the dust from grinding. Ruth says 'My need
was not physical', even though her pain very much was. She
points to loneliness, her worries and her rejection for promotion
as reasons why she experienced such severe menstrual problems.

What they are saying is that how you feel can profoundly affect
your health. They endorse the view that we are damaged by
physical agents, by toxic chemicals, poor food, pollution, damp,
tobacco and so on, but almost all of them speak from a perspective which assumes that a deeper understanding of what makes
us ill must recognize that our relationships with each other and
our feelings about ourselves somehow affect our vulnerability to
illness. They are saying that our everyday experience bears on
our health in ways which are far more complex and subtle than
the crude correlations of epidemiology[3] would lead us to expect;
and that to understand why we get ill we must look at our *social*
as well as our physical environment.[4] Some readers may feel
uneasy with this point of view, fearing that to enter the realm of
feelings is to leave the sphere of politics. This is not the view of
any of the people interviewed. Each of them makes it very clear
that they see the forces bearing on their feelings as the same ones
which determine whether lead is put in petrol, how much is spent

on housing, or what controls there are on cancer-causing substances. The pursuit of profit shapes the health-destructive organization of work in Baden's factory, just as it leads to the disregard for life in Andrew's. Vera's feelings of demoralization and powerlessness, Ruth's loneliness, George's sense of being like a spare part, are as intimately linked to conditions of life determined by social forces as Les's TB or Shan's collapse with the solder.

Class experience

A second important point which many of the people interviewed make is that to understand the effect of people's lives on their health, you have to look at the inter-relatedness of all the things going on in them. Shan points out that the women who were most seriously depressed at work were those who were also coping with children and sick relatives at home. Baden says that assembly work is worse if you have got home worries, as it gives you nothing to take your mind off them. Vera argues that when jobs are threatened, women face the strain, not only of the worry of losing their own jobs, but the drain of giving added emotional support to their husbands, whose jobs are also likely to be at risk. Ruth sees her pain as a result of compounded experiences, including not getting promoted, being worried about how to find the money for the mortgage, being under pressure of work at college, feeling resentful of her unemployed children, being lonely, partly because she was on a course with women half her age and partly because she had moved to a new neighbourhood, and sensing the discrimination against her as a black woman, which is a factor which recurs in every aspect of her life.

Sometimes when people become ill a cause can easily be attributed. When someone gets lung cancer in Andrew's factory, the workers know it is very likely to do with BisCME. But far more often it is impossible to say if it's the job, or the kids, or the house, or the husband, or the social security, or the loss of someone you were close to. As Vera said, 'What makes us ill is a combination of pressures which come with being working class, for God's sake.'

Wellbeing is tied up with class experience. And that class experience cannot be easily reduced into neat compartments. It can't even be boiled down to income. Although how much money you get is clearly a crucial factor, it is not the whole problem. Making your wages up by overtime leaves you even more exhausted. Even decent wages cannot compensate for a lifetime of soul-destroying work. High redundancy payments cannot compensate for feeling on the scrapheap. Having a home with a garden cannot compensate for feeling isolated in it. The problem is not just how wealth is distributed, but how it is produced.

Health and experience

Having been taught all our lives that illness is caused by germs,[5] or by other pathogens like tobacco, a view of health and illness which says that how well we are is bound up with the way we experience our lives comes as a shock. Yet outside of mainstream medical thinking there has been considerable support for this view over many years. Specialists in social medicine have long recognized the notion of the 'vulnerability of the host', the idea that whether you catch an infection depends on how run-down and vulnerable you are as well as the presence of the germ. It is well known, for instance, that not everyone who is exposed to tuberculosis bacilli will get tuberculosis. Those who develop the illness are the ones in whom resistance is lower. A study by Meyer and Haggerty in 1962 found that children were four times more likely to get a sore throat if they had witnessed a distressing event such as a bad car accident or their father losing his job.[6] Now that there are fewer infectious diseases and more chronic and degenerative diseases, the concept of vulnerability of the host has been widened to imply general vulnerability to illness and used to explain differences in mortality rates, for instance between the single, the married, the widowed and the divorced. Emotional and physiological factors are linked in far more sophisticated ways than we are led to believe. Bereavement has recently been shown to affect the functioning of the lymphocytes which maintain immunity against bacteria viruses and the growth of cancer cells.[7] A study of 200 men in the United States found that among the fifty-nine men judged to have 'good mental health', two died or became chronically ill, while among the forty-eight men judged to have the worst mental health, eighteen died or became chronically ill.[8]

It is also widely accepted within medical sociology that people's conditions of life affect their vulnerability to mental and physical illness. Medical sociologists have emphasized particularly that as well as looking at factors damaging our health we need to consider 'protective factors', the things which help us resist illness. When you think of all that the people in the interviews were up against, their resilience is remarkable. In view of the riskiness of the outside world, we need an explanation not just for why we get sick, but how we survive at all. Sociologists stress the importance of intimate relationships as protection against illness. There is considerable evidence that being able to confide and to share emotions prevents them being internalized as mental or physical illness. The experience of psychotherapists who have found that therapy can bring relief of physical illness backs up the link between our experience and our health. In many Eastern philosophies the idea that life and health are intimately bound up is a common theme. And in many alternative forms of healing practised in the West, particularly naturopathy and homeopathy, exploring what is happening in the rest of your life is a central part of the healing process.

Among those whose recognize the link between health and experience, there are of course many different points of view. Some argue that although what is happening in our lives may influence our vulnerability to illness, there must also be a concrete physical agent – a germ or pathogen – to trigger it. Others argue that our emotions can affect our bodies directly without the mediation of physical agents (a view we tend to share). There is a debate, too, about whether our state of mind affects only our *general* liability to illness or whether particular emotional states can give rise to specific illness, ulcers, headaches or whatever. And of course there are many people who make the connection between health and feelings without making the other necessary connection between feelings and the conditions of our lives.[9]

Production and reproduction

It may be that in looking at health and illness we have been trapped because the only evidence available to us was the evidence of epidemiology, which has been about trying to track down the links between specific illnesses and specific causes, such as the link between lung cancer and cigarettes. To explain the vast class differences in health we must look beyond the known risk factors established by epidemiological research to less easily measurable and quantifiable aspects of our lives. This does not mean no longer taking pollution, exposure to carcinogens or the dangers of motor vehicles seriously. Differential exposure to them is a crucial part of the explanation of the class pattern of ill health. But it does mean recognizing that a more comprehensive explanation must take account not only of the physical dangers of living in a capitalist society but the way the social relations of that society damage us too. To explore what is making us ill we have to look at the relationships between women and men, between white and black people, between employee and employer, and we have to look at the way work is organized, the hours of work, the division of labour, how caring for children, sick and very elderly people, making food and doing housework is organized, how houses are built, how cities are planned, and who decides, who is in control and where the power lies.

When we say that so much of our ill health is rooted in the

social relations of capitalism, we are not saying that all ill health comes from capitalist workplaces. Inside the factory it becomes clear how irreconcilable the raw logic of capital is with the conditions for our health. Shan, George, Baden and Andrew each illustrate how employers profit at the expense of our ill health. To look at what happens in factories is important, because it is in that fundamental antagonism of health against profit – that wasting of our bodies for their ends – that the dynamic of our whole society is rooted. The social relations of capitalism extend far beyond the factory, however. Capital's struggle to create the conditions for its own survival has shaped, and continually re-shapes, the social structures within which we conduct our lives. Capital's interest is not just in making profits now, but in ensuring the continuation of a system in which it can carry on doing so in the future, which means resisting our resistance and attempting to structure our lives in a way which limits our capacity to fight back. Filling our heads with nonsense, isolating us and dividing us from one another, making us feel frightened, undermining our confidence, ensuring our powerlessness and destroying our solidarity are all part and parcel of the process of ensuring the continuation of the conditions in which capitalism can survive. We find capital's social relations not just in the factory – in the hierarchy, and in the organization of work – but in other kinds of workplace, in schools, in social security offices, in council offices, in hospitals (as we will discuss in Part Two), in government departments, and in our intimate relations with each other. The experiences which give rise to our ill health – the loneliness, the powerlessness, the alienation – are the pre-conditions of capitalism's survival. In examining the roots of our ill health we must explore both what happens within capitalist production and the processes by which that mode of production is reproduced.

Eight dimensions

In thinking about what damages our health and what keeps us well, eight key dimensions emerge:

1. *How much we are exposed to a hazardous environment, both inside and outside of work.* Andrew's story graphically illustrates how hazardous work can be. He points out how many untested chemicals are currently in use in factories and how many products now in use may also turn out to be dangerous to the consumer. While there is a great deal more research that could be done, already much is known – about the dangers of work processes, including toxic chemicals, hazardous machinery and noise, of the industrial production of food, or motor vehicles and polluted air – which is not being acted on.

2. *How exhausted our work inside and outside the home makes us, and how much time and space we have for recuperation.* Ethel remarks that since bonus schemes were introduced her sons seem to come home tireder than her husband used to. Shan describes the exhaustion of sweatshop work, especially where there is no union protection. She also points out that where women are working a double shift – going out to work then doing the housework, as Ethel was, particularly in the period when she was going twice a day to do office cleaning – the exhaustion is intensified. Looking after children can also be exhausting in itself, especially if it means losing sleep. How long we work, how intensely we have to work and how much sleep we lose is a measure of our exploitation. George points out the evils of overtime and shiftwork. The double shift, productivity deals and speed-ups, shiftwork, overtime and working unsocial hours all damage our health. In stealing our time[10] and energy, capital destroys our bodies too.

3. *How much money we take home.* Overtime, bonus schemes and the rest may be exhausting, but they are often the only way to make enough money to live on. Earnings are crucial. Of all the factors in the Whitehall study, income proved a much more

powerful predictor of whether a man got heart disease than all the physiological measures, including blood plasma cholesterol and blood pressure. In the *Longitudinal Study* a combination of the number of cars in the household and whether people live in a council house or an owner-occupied house, both very crude measures of income, was found to be the most powerful discriminator of mortality rates.[11] Money buys housing, which also means space so we don't get on top of one another. It buys gardens, which means having somewhere safe for children to play. It buys weekends in the country and holidays for relaxation. It brings freedom from financial worries and opens up the number of choices you can make about your life and thus the degree to which you can feel in control of it. All of these are very important to health.

4. *How many worries we have and how deep and sustained they are.* Worries about work, about losing your job, about your children's future, about the dangers of walking in the streets, about how to pay the bills, about getting the gas cut off, about breaking the law to make ends meet, and about illness can all affect our health. It is worse when they all come together and if there seems no way out.

5. *How hopeful or hopeless we feel.* How hopeful we feel for the future affects how much we are prepared to invest in our own health now. Feeling positive about things is a precondition of taking exercise, changing what you eat, or giving up addictions, including tranquillizers, food and tobacco. If you don't see things getting better, if you can't look forward to holidays, or getting a job, or being able to enjoy having children or retirement, if you feel stuck, taking an interest in your own wellbeing is the last thing you want to do.

6. *How powerless or powerful we feel.* Both Ruth and Vera identify their own powerlessness as a factor in their ill health. Vera talks of women not feeling they have a right to influence events beyond their own front door. What we want is to be powerful not in the sense of controlling other people, but in the

sense of feeling in control of our own lives. We want a fair share
in decisions which affect us, personal space and autonomy. The
term oppression connotes a bowed back. We bear in our bodies
the class and gender relations of the wider society. Every time
we are assumed to be ignorant or stupid and are told what to do,
our bodies hold that pain. A sense of not being able to take
initiatives, or not knowing which way to turn, drains our spirits.

7. *How bored or alienated we feel.* George and Baden describe
how destructive monotonous work can be, and how not feeling
in control of what you are making, whether it is a tractor or a
machine tool, leaves a hollow feeling. They both say that making
something you can take no pride in is soul-destroying. Not
enjoying your work, feeling your time is not your own, can in
itself be destructive of health. So can the boredom of unemployment. And stopping work after a lifetime of work seems to kill
a lot of men, who, like George's brother, find themselves facing
a terrible vacuum.

8. *How lonely or loved we feel.* The loss of someone close to
you, as Ruth lost her friend, has long been recognized as having
consequences for our health. Spouses often die within a short
period of one another. Loss is also a major factor in depression
and in increasing vulnerability to illness. Equally, having someone to talk to and share feelings with can make us less likely to
become ill. But it is not just very intimate and family relationships which affect us; so does having workmates and neighbours
to be friends with. Vera contrasts the isolation of the tower block
with the friendliness of the old neighbourhoods. Ethel also
regrets her present isolation, looking back on the time when she
was able to sit out with her neighbours: 'There was more happiness and more laughter.' Shan argues that in Guyana, although
people were working for a boss, they worked together and
enjoyed each other's company, whereas the working relationships she has found in Britain have not been so good, with
workers turned against each other by piece-work and having no
time for chatting. Her complaint goes beyond the factory. She

indicts our whole society for the constraints it puts on friendship and sociability. Medical sociologists have identified going out to work as a 'protective factor' against illness for both women and men. George regrets losing the gregariousness of his work, for all that he hated it in other ways. Baden complains that the new style of production cuts off almost all human contact, despite working among thousands of people.

We tend to concentrate on the negative poles of the eight dimensions. But their positive poles – a clean and safe environment, time for rest and recreation, reasonable living standards, freedom from chronic worry, hope for the future, self-confidence and autonomy, fulfilling work, and opportunities for friendship, support and intimacy – also provide a framework for thinking about the minimum conditions for health a reasonable society should work for.

This model of illness and health should explain why some people stay well, as well as why others get ill. Men at the top of society do not have to work or live in a hazardous environment. Making all those decisions is hard work and stressful, but they also enjoy their work and find time for relaxation. They have the money for country cottages and get time off to take holidays abroad. They may be under pressure, but they also feel in control. They confide in their wives and secretaries. They are proud of their families, and they probably don't have to worry very much about their future. They worry – who doesn't? – about their work and decisions they may have to make about their lives, but these are usually temporary worries, worries about which way out rather than not having a way out. In later life they are unlikely to find themselves suddenly on the scrapheap. They reduce their workload a bit. They may formally retire, but they don't often entirely let go of the work that provides them with a sense of being needed, of identity, a place in the world, stimulation and company.[12]

The dimensions should also go some way to explaining the differences in the patterns of women's and men's health. In the official statistics, the class differences in mortality rates do not show such extremes among women as among men, but at the same time there is a sharper divide between women married to manual workers and women married to men in professional jobs. The lack of extremities may well reflect the common threads which link the lives of all women. The possibilities and choices for women at the top of society are very much greater than for women at the bottom, but we share a sense of powerlessness and the hurt of our oppression. At the same time the better relative position of the male skilled manual worker, in relation to his wife, may reflect the stronger bargaining position, sense of power and confidence which trade unionism has historically conferred more widely on men than on women.

Slump and boom

As children we learned that as society develops, so does progress, and that with progress comes better health. The picture painted by the eight people we interviewed suggests a very different state of affairs, however. All eight referred to the deteriorating conditions of life brought by the present crisis. For Ethel, Baden and Vera it is a central theme. Ethel highlights the consequences of declining living standards and the insecurity of work. Baden describes the alienation and soullessness of the modern high-technology factory. Vera demands that we pay attention to our deteriorating expectations of our life and health.

A lot of fuss has been made over the past few years about the consequences to our health of unemployment, and undoubtedly it is health-damaging in some ways. But what we learn from the interviews is that at the moment our health is being destroyed not by an economic crisis which has fallen on us like an Act of God, but *by the measures being taken in the bid to resolve the crisis.* Our problem is not just unemployment and falling living standards, which are meant to be the 'temporary' costs of the industrial shake-out, but the brave new world itself, the high-productivity work, the new technology and the privatization of personal life. Baden's life is how it is meant to be, just as George's life was how it was meant to be in the post-war boom. These men are not part of some residual category that society half-recognizes it is failing. They are the mainstream. Their troubles have their roots in up-turns, not down-turns. When we hear on the telly about restoring the productivity of British industry, more Massey Fergusons is what they have in mind. According to ruling values, what's happening in Baden's factory is a success story. Measures which will increase our powerlessness and loneliness, including the further privatization of family life, the smashing of solidarity within and between unions, are central to the Thatcherite vision.

The conditions of life which damage our health are not a by-product of capitalism going through a bad phase, nor the result of inequalities in the way society's goodies are distributed. They are intimately linked with capitalist production and the repro-duction of the conditions for capitalism's survival. Our attention is drawn to the class pattern of health by its distribution between the 'social classes' as defined in official statistics. But to under-stand the pattern we need to look at it in terms not of how misfortune is distributed but how it is produced. Health is like wealth; the problem is fundamentally less to do with how it is spread out than how it is created. Finally the class categories which make sense are not those of official statistics, but of everyday politics. The health of the majority of people is not compatible with the present form of organization of our society.

Part Two

Who Cares?

4 Common Treatment

My sister is having an asthma attack. She usually copes with it using an inhaler. When it really gets bad she takes the same drug in the form of pink pills. She will not take more than half at a time. It makes her body shake and she feels anxious and panicky. This time the drugs have not worked. She sits in front of the television struggling for breath. All day she has been like this. She does not want the doctor to come. Having been in hospital once before with asthma, she insists that at all costs she will not go in again.

As the evening wears on, her strength seems to fade. She seems to be losing her fight to breathe. 'Will it ever end', she moans and now does not protest when we call the doctor. As he prepares an injection we tell him that on previous occasions it has made her sick, but he does not seem to hear. She is sick, but seems a little better. As she goes to bed we assume it is all over.

Through the night her breathing is still hard work and she cannot sleep. In the early morning we call the doctor again, but the message comes back from the answering service to take her straight to hospital. I feel cheated of a chance to discuss whether it is really necessary. Between breaths, Caroline says again 'I don't want to go. It is too upsetting.'

In the dark the digital clock registers the passing minutes. Finally I realize I cannot take responsibility for keeping her at home. I insist and she accedes. As we wait for the ambulance Caroline says 'I am glad it is morning. There is something better about going in the morning than being taken away in the night.'

I'm glad to see the ambulance. It's light now and as we chat on the way to the hospital, I feel the anxiety of the night lifting.

When we arrive in the casualty department, I'm pleased to be there. Having spent the summer on hospital picket lines, reporting the health workers' industrial action, I feel close to and respectful of NHS staff. Being with the ambulancemen has brought those feelings back. Arriving at the hospital feels like coming home, but the nurse at the desk does not return my greeting.

The doctor, a young woman of about my age, addresses Caroline in pidgin English. Either this is the form of address she adopts for all her patients in our predominantly working-class multiracial community, or she assumes that, in having temporary difficulty speaking, Caroline is hard of hearing. They put a little tube in her arm with a green plastic top. She is to be given aminophylline, the same injection she had before, hydrocortisone, a steroid, and another drug to stop blood clogging up the plug. I tell the doctor aminophylline makes my sister sick, but again she does not seem to hear. During the X-ray Caroline is sick again.

After the drugs, the wheezing subsides. We gather that she is to be admitted, but no one actually tells us what is going to happen, explains why she needs to be kept in or indicates how long it is likely to be for. While we wait for them to find a bed, we chat with the nurse. She has asthma too, sometimes. So do I. Idly the three of us talk it over. Could it be cats or stress? This is chit-chat. What might be causing it all is something the doctors do not raise at any stage during her subsequent stay in hospital. The conversation drifts. The nurse is leaving the NHS and going abroad. She has had enough of long hours, low pay, and exhausting work and, with more local hospitals closing, it looks as if things will get worse, not better. A second young doctor finally arrives. There are problems finding a bed, as the hospital is very full. 'There is not really a shortage of beds for young people, who this kind of hospital is really for', he says. 'The problem is all the old people who should really be in geriatric hospitals who are blocking up the beds.' Finally a bed is found and Caroline is wheeled off through the maze of dilapidated Victorian buildings.

In the five days she is in hospital Caroline neither eats nor sleeps. Most of the women in her ward are elderly. Two sisters in their eighties occupy the end beds. One is blind and mentally confused; through the night she cries out to her sister. A third woman is seriously mentally disturbed. She's on the ward because there is a shortage of places for 'psycho-geriatrics'. All day she shouts and swears. She smears faeces in the toilet and shits on the ward floor. The other patients are upset because she steals fruit from them with dirty hands. The shouting is one reason why Caroline cannot sleep. Nausea deters her from eating. I cannot tempt her with food from home.

At first Caroline is on a drip to counteract the dehydration caused by being sick with the aminophylline. Every four hours, day and night, she is given a very big dose of salbutamol, the same drug that is in the ordinary inhaler. It makes her shake and brings on all the feelings and physiological sensations of an acute anxiety attack. She says it makes her feel like something terrible is going to happen. Neither doctors nor nurses note or ask how she feels after taking it. Her distress is increased by the tiredness, the effect of the drugs and the loneliness of being in hospital. A sense of despair that neither doctors nor nurses appear to care how she is feeling is intensified by the knowledge of how overworked and underpaid they are. She feels she has no right to expect more of them.

The woman in the next bed cries frequently. A bit of her spine has crumbled. She feels she has gone from lively middle age to being an old woman overnight. She and her friend used to have such a good time together, but now she won't be able to get out of the house, she tells us. There is no one to look after her at home. The doctors have told her she will never be better and there is nothing they can do. The woman on the other side has an undiagnosed chest pain. She was admitted on Saturday, but there was no room for her in the ward she should have been in.

By Wednesday she has not yet been seen by a senior doctor. It is only when she threatens to discharge herself that one turns up. Further down the ward there are two Indian women, one of whom speaks little English. The nurses say loudly in front of her 'She is not very intelligent, you know.' The other woman's husband works shifts and can only come out of visiting hours. This also meets with the nurses' disapproval.

Each day we look at the chart hanging at the bottom of the bed. The graph showing Caroline's lung capacity shows a steadily upward trend. As well as the salbutamol, she is now on antibiotics and steroid tablets too. Having had such a big dose of steroids when she came in, she can't be taken straight off. One day, when we are looking at the chart, the ward sister comes over to us and takes it away. I know how 'know-it-all' patients and relatives are viewed, but we end up having a noisy row. I say it is Caroline's body and she should have a right to know about it. Clutching the chart to her chest, she says it is wrong to read papers belonging to the hospital and the staff will answer any questions. Afterwards we go over the arguments in hushed voices. The nurses do not have the answers and the doctors seem inaccessible. The problem is that the doctors only see you once every three days, and the nurses cannot give an opinion, for instance about whether all the drugs are really necessary. 'It is all wrong', Caroline says. 'It goes back to the way the work is divided up between doctors and nurses. What we need is a cross between a doctor and a nurse.'

Discharged, she sits at home. She has no asthma. The permanent steroids see to that. But she is weak, listless and has a far-away look. Is she recovering from the asthma, from the drugs or from the experience in hospital? It is impossible to tell. There is something about the pain of it all that I cannot fathom. The hospital have abated a crisis. But now she must heal from the wound it has caused her.[1]

5 What Can Medicine Do?

A doctor had not a lot of time to discuss this body that you live in and see whether you were prepared to have a go at prevention. You just went to the doctor's when your poor old broken body got so bad that you had to go and see about getting it mended. He would patch you up and send you back to work. There is no scheme for you to go and have some fantastic cure, because there are no cures.

George Taylor

In Part One we did not say much about doctors and hospitals. Too often, as soon as anyone mentions health and illness, we conjure up images of surgeries, clinics, white coats and stethoscopes, and this distracts us from thinking about the causes of our health problems. But it is time to look at how the medicine practised in the NHS responds to all our ailments. What answers does it have? What is there in its store cupboard of pills, potions, blood tests, X-rays and operations to heal us?

When the health service was first established by the post-war Labour government, the politicians believed that once health care was accessible to all, ill health would drastically decline and doctors would put themselves out of business. Far from tailing off, however, medical effort has multiplied. Since 1949 the number of people going in and out of hospital has almost doubled.[1] Spending on the NHS has more than tripled in real terms.[2] The pharmaceutical industry has grown from a few minor companies to become Britain's fourth largest export earner.[3] Medical technology has also become big business. The pharmaceutical companies' research budget (which now accounts for over half the spending on medical research in Britain) has risen fifteen-fold.[4] In the past twenty years this growth of activity has accelerated. Daily the newspapers report the triumphs of medicine – 'Tumour boy in miracle op' – and the medical press joins in – 'New hope for heart programme'. Heart transplants, bone marrow transplants, laser surgery, test-tube babies and interferon are particularly celebrated. We are left with the impression that although there may be outstanding problems research has yet to conquer, day by day medicine strides forward. A booklet with a shining gold cover celebrates the fiftieth anniversary of the Association of the British Pharmaceutical Industry[5]:

> In this year of the Association of the British Pharmaceutical Industry's Golden Jubilee, member companies can justifiably be proud of their pre-eminent role in the evolution of chemotherapy over the last 50 years ... the inventive genius of the industry – reflected in the fact that of 150 most popularly prescribed drugs in 1977 only 22 were available 31 years earlier – is such that, given research funds, scientific and technical challenges are unlikely to prove insuperable and society can look forward to the introduction of major new medicines ...

Can we share the confidence of the tabloids and the drug industry that it is only a matter of time before medicine comes up with new cures? And what assessment can be made of its present contribution to making and keeping us well?

The modern scourges

More medical effort probably goes into research on, and treatment for, cancer than for any other illness. In the past twenty years treatment has improved the likelihood of survival from childhood cancer, some forms of leukaemia and Hodgkin's disease. There have been dramatic increases in the survival rate for children with Wilms' tumour, acute lymphoblastic leukaemia and Hodgkin's disease, and the overall death rate from cancer for children under fourteen has dropped by a quarter since 1961. In 1966 one in five people with skin cancer died within five years; now almost all survive. In 1971 only one in five people with acute leukaemia could expect to be alive within five years; now almost two in five will survive.[6] But, sadly, these forms of cancer make up only a small proportion of all cancers. Less than one in a hundred cases of cancer are skin cancer, and acute leukaemia accounts for only three in a thousand.

For most other forms of cancer, the survival rate has improved little. The distressing fact is that still less than one in ten people with cancer of the lung, stomach, oesophagus or pancreas (four of the most common forms of cancer) survives for more than five years.[7] And even where there appears to have been an improvement in the survival statistics, for instance in breast cancer and bladder cancer, this may reflect an earlier date of diagnosis rather than an overall improvement in life expectancy. All the resources going into the treatment of cancer may be giving us a false impression of its efficacy.

Table 4 *Cancer survival: the number of people surviving five years or more out of every 100 diagnosed with cancer*

Site of cancer	Women				Men			
	1947	1958	1966	1975	1947	1958	1966	1975
Pancreas	n.a.	2	2	3.6	n.a.	2	2	2.8
Oesophagus	n.a.	4	5	8.1	n.a.	2	4	5.6
Lung	3	4	5	6.6	2	6	6	7
Stomach	n.a.	5	6	7.4	n.a.	7	6	6.9
Brain	n.a.	20	27	15.1	n.a.	16	20	12.2
Colon	18	25	27	29.5	15	23	25	31.3
Rectum	22	27	30	30.6	17	26	29	30.6
Ovary	n.a.	21	24	23.4	—	—	—	—
Prostate	—	—	—	—	24	27	32	35.1
Bladder	n.a.	29	41	47.8	n.a.	33	45	54.3
Breast	37	44	53	57.4	—	—	—	—
Cervix	35	43	67	51.7	—	—	—	—
Skin	77	84	81	97.4	78	86	80	96.4

Sources: *Cancer Statistics 1971* (OPCS Series MB No. 1, HMSO, 1979) and *Cancer Incidence, Survival and Mortality Rates* (OPCS Series SMPS No. 43, HMSO, 1981).

In some instances surgery can make the cancer less distressing. Operations for bowel cancer can be effective in removing obstructions. Whether surgery can remove the cancer altogether is more doubtful, as although the primary site may be removed (for instance in cancer of the breast, womb or intestine), fatal secondary cancers often develop. Radical mastectomy, which involves removing muscles within the chest as well as up into the armpit along with the breast, has become less popular with surgeons since they learned that this operation confers no greater chance of survival than simple mastectomy. Now, however, there is similar evidence that removing the whole breast may be no more effective than removing just the lump. And some doctors are now questioning whether all treatments for breast cancer are equally *in*effective. Examination of the survival statistics for lung cancer has also led to fewer operations to remove the lung.

Radiotherapy can enable people to be less immobilized by their illness, and powerful drugs can now relieve cancer pain. Doctors acknowledge, however, that radiotherapy is primarily a palliative treatment. It is not a cure and in most instances does not increase life expectancy. All treatments for cancer are unpleasant, and there is some evidence they may be over-used. Major surgery is always a shock to the system and may reduce the body's capacity to fight off illness. Radiotherapy gives rise to the symptoms of radiation sickness, including reduced appetite, nausea and weakness. Recently there has been particular concern among doctors about the extensive use of the new cytotoxic drugs, which cause nausea and hair loss as well as weakening the body's resistance, before their value has properly been established by clinical trials. Routine therapy in many hospitals now involves administering these cell-killing drugs in a dose several times the known lethal limit for humans, followed several hours later by a 'rescue' dose to neutralize the effect before too much damage is done.

People who themselves have cancer often express doubts about continuing treatment which is upsetting and unlikely to be effective. Some nurses have also expressed worries about the unwise use of cancer treatment, particularly surgery in the elderly. Doctors, nurses and other health workers with first-hand knowledge of the side effects and likely outcome of treatment often say privately that there are some treatments they would personally refuse. Securing more weeks or months of life may be at the cost of the quality of that life, they argue. Other doctors have been more outspoken. Dick Richards, in his recent book *The Topic of Cancer*,[8] describes the current techniques of 'cut, burn and poison' as giving rise to 'wanton suffering'. In his introduction to the book he says:

For twenty years as a family physician in the same town in England, I carried out or supervised the orthodox medical cancer therapies I had been taught. They didn't really work. Speaking with the advantages of hindsight, it now seems remarkable that I never seriously questioned the methods just the same. Neither did any of my colleagues so far as I recall. Time and again a patient I'd known for years got cancer, was operated on and treated with radiation and drugs, and was returned to my care. The same routine then followed with remorseless repetition. I would begin the hopeless task of presiding over that patient's decline, telling reassuring lies, and giving more and more pain-relieving drugs until death ensued. What about those who got better? There were not enough to write about.

Heart disease

The possibilities for medical intervention in heart disease are also limited. Once someone has had a heart attack there is little that doctors and hospitals can do for him or her. Four in ten people who have heart attacks die within a month, and more than half of these are sudden deaths for which no intervention is possible. Two in a hundred are saved by resuscitation.[9] Those who have these near-fatal heart attacks usually go on to have a second heart attack in the following year or two. Going into hospital after a heart attack may be necessary for the care of that person, but studies have shown that being in hospital rather than at home sadly does not improve your chances of survival.[10] In recent years there has been a growth of specialized coronary care units, equipped with electronic devices to monitor cardiac rhythms, but so far these have not been proved to reduce the likelihood of death. Research on the value of specially equipped coronary care ambulances which have been introduced in some areas has not clearly demonstrated their effectiveness in saving lives.[11] On a more positive note, recent data from the USA does indicate that the reduced death rate from heart attacks is due not to fewer people having heart disease, but fewer people dying from it. If this is the case, then it will be necessary to establish what innovations in health care are contributing to the reduced number of deaths. Some studies suggest that where there is public education about the need for immediate resuscitation, combined with coronary care ambulances, mortality rates have fallen.

Heart transplants may be news, but there is no evidence that on average they can confer a longer life, and many doctors are sceptical about them. Newspapers make a lot of the operations, but rarely report the patient's subsequent death. Of the seventy-eight heart transplants carried out at Papworth and Harefield up until August 1982 thirty-eight people have already died.[12] Coronary by-pass surgery is beneficial for a small proportion of people at risk from coronary heart disease. The procedure in which a vein is taken from the leg and sewn into the heart wall relieves the pain of severe angina and, in a smaller group with particular sorts of coronary disease, can prolong life. There is evidence, however, that this operation is sometimes carried out without benefit, particularly in the United States. Some researchers have estimated as many as nine out of ten coronary by-pass operations in the USA may be unnecessary.[13] Pacemakers which artificially stimulate the rhythm of the heart can prolong life. Again, however, there have been suggestions that these operations are now sometimes over-used.[14]

Everyday troubles

With many of the more ordinary health problems of everyday life medicine cannot claim better success. There is no cure for rheumatism, arthritis and most forms of back pain. No cure for chronic bronchitis, emphysema and other chronic chest problems. No permanent cure for most digestive problems, including ulcers, colitis and chronic diarrhoea. No cure for the degenerative illnesses like multiple sclerosis and motor neurone disease. No cure for virus infections like glandular fever. And no cure for mental illness. Of course some of these conditions can improve or even get better altogether with changes in people's lives or for reasons that do not seem apparent at the time – long-term virus infections, for instance, can last for several years and then disappear completely – but the improvement can rarely be attributed to medicine.

In practice what medicine sets out to do for chronic conditions is to relieve pain, discomfort and immobility. Sometimes this can bring about dramatic alleviation of symptoms. At other times the solution offered may be ineffective or give rise to further complications.

When bronchodilators for asthma, for instance, were introduced it seemed like a great success story for pharmaceutical research. The inhalers were welcomed with open arms by asthma sufferers, as they can completely take away a distressing attack in a matter of seconds. But the initial effect of their introduction in the sixties was to triple the death rate.[15] Now, following the replacement of the early inhalers with a type less damaging to the heart, the death rate has returned to the level it was at when the inhalers were first introduced; but it has not actually fallen. It is also possible that reliance on inhalers may lead to the reinforcement of breathing patterns which compound the problem in the long term.

The invention of cimetidine, commercially called Tagamet, for gastric and duodenal ulcers was also hailed as a medical triumph. Cimetidine relieves the pain of an ulcer almost immediately and stops internal bleeding. But it also leads to the production of nitrosamines, known to cause stomach cancer in animals. For this reason it is recommended that the drug should be given for only four to six weeks, followed by a maintenance dose for six months. Once the drug is stopped, duodenal ulcers return to four out of five people.[16] Cimetidine treatment may make the return of ulcers more likely than if the ulcer is left to heal itself, admittedly a more painful business. There is also considerable evidence that, despite the possible cancer risk, cimetidine is being given to people with non-specific stomach problems before it has definitely been established they have an ulcer. In 1980 the *Sunday Times* reported that 11 million people had been put on it in 100 countries.[17]

Cimetidine has been a relative success story among treatments for digestive problems. There is no cure for chronic bowel problems. The only effective treatment for ulcerative colitis in more serious cases is to remove the infected part of the intestine, which usually involves replacing the rectum with an opening in the front of the abdomen. Surgery is also the last resort in chronic inflammation of the small intestine. Often the first operation has to be followed by further operations in which more and more of the intestine is cut away.

Arthritis is another everyday health problem affecting millions for which medicine offers no cure. Until recently there was no better palliation than aspirin, but since the mid-1960s the market has been flooded with a whole range of new non-steroid anti-inflammatory drugs for pains in the bones and joints. Since 1977, eleven new brands have been added to the list. Extravagant media coverage raised sufferers' hopes.[18] Although the drugs can be of limited usefulness when such high doses of aspirin have to be given that stomach problems occur, there is no evidence that the new drugs provide better pain relief. And these drugs themselves can often cause stomach problems. Recently one of the newest, Opren, which had been promoted as being specially suited to older people, was withdrawn after over sixty deaths associated with the drug among elderly people.

For very severe crippling rheumatoid arthritis the last-resort treatment is penicillamine tablets or injections of gold. These do improve the pain and retard the progression of the disease, but there is a risk of possible side effects. With gold, one in twenty people has severe and occasionally fatal side effects, and the treatment often leads to eventual kidney failure.[19]

Mental illnesses have come to be defined as the proper sphere of medicine and in the past twenty years a range of powerful drugs used in the treatment of anxiety, depression and schizophrenia have been introduced. The new drugs for schizophrenia and other psychotic conditions[20] reduce people's unusual behaviour and outward symptoms of distress, often leaving them withdrawn and apathetic. The drugs are of great benefit to the health service because they improve the 'management' of patients, who can be sent home between acute crises rather than take up a hospital bed. But there is no evidence that these drugs are healing. Many people are given them for a lifetime. Some psychotherapists also argue that the drugs prevent the healing process which can occur through a period of madness.[21] Antipsychotic drugs often give rise to uncontrollable body movements, which can sometimes be relieved by, and are sometimes made worse by, giving a second counter-active drug. When a person comes off these drugs, the shaking can persist and sometimes becomes worse.

When tranquillizers were first introduced they seemed the perfect medication. They changed people's moods with very few side effects and were judged to be non-addictive. As a result they have been widely prescribed for many people who come to the doctor with unhappiness and worries about ill health which appear to have no specific internal cause. Something like one in fifty of the adult population in Britain take tranquillizers permanently. In Britain, as in most other Western countries, one in five women and one in ten men take tranquillizers at some time in the course of a year. Despite the claims of the pharmaceutical companies, tranquillizers are now recognized by pharmacologists and specialist doctors to be addictive. After months and years of constant use they usually lose their mood-changing effect, but giving them up often involves frightening withdrawal symptoms, including sweating, shaking, panic attacks, insomnia and lack of confidence. It has been conservatively estimated that one hundred thousand people in Britain are addicted to tranquillizers.[22] The other effect of these drugs, of course, is to make more people put up with intolerable situations; they reduce our capacity to challenge what is happening to us.

Many common, recurrent women's illnesses also defy medication. Cystitis and pelvic inflammatory disease are two of the most troublesome, often recurring again and again despite courses of antibiotics. There is no clear evidence that the 'D and C', the most common gynaecological operation, is of value in treating minor menstrual disorders.[23] There is also evidence that hysterectomies are sometimes performed without good cause.[24] In the United States the hysterectomy rate is three times greater than in Britain, without clear evidence that American women are better off for it. It has been suggested that doctors' readiness to remove the womb may be linked to a subconscious view that after child-bearing it is a redundant part. Removing the womb, as Ruth discovered, is a major operation, which can take many months to recover from. It also frequently brings irreversible hormonal and emotional changes and affects women's feelings about themselves and their sexuality.

Life-savers

When it comes to accidents and emergencies there is a lot that medicine can do. Over the past twenty years techniques of emergency treatment have been greatly improved. New developments in anaesthesia enable longer and more complex operations to be carried out on people of all ages. The work of the heart and lungs can now be sustained during long operations and the body's functions can be monitored far more accurately. It is now possible to put people back together again after the most serious accidents. Without this technology the death rate from car accidents would have been far higher even than it is today.

Emergency operations for abdominal obstruction, acute appendicitis and perforated peptic ulcers can all be life-saving. Many of the operations we wait patiently for on the waiting list can also restore us to normal health, including hernia and prolapse repair and removal of the enlarged prostate. These non-life-threatening conditions can be seriously disabling. Routine operations can in a matter of days completely take away conditions which have been the source of considerable discomfort and pain. Operations to remove varicose veins can take the pain away for several years, although the problem often returns in time. Kidney dialysis keeps thousands of people alive whose kidneys have failed, and kidney transplants extend the lives of many who would otherwise have died. Hip replacement operations can give many more years of mobility to older people who would otherwise have been housebound and in permanent pain. The removal of cataracts can restore sight.

Many lives have also been prolonged through better understanding of how hormones work and the action of the glands that produce them. Hormone replacement therapy is now used to treat glands controlling the metabolism, growth and sex hormones. Thyroid problems (like the one Ethel suffered) in particular can now be much better controlled by hormone treatment. Diabetes, by far the most common of these conditions, has of course been successfully treated by insulin since long before the present explosion of medical research. For people who develop diabetes in childhood, insulin has brought a longer and less troublesome life. But even insulin cannot be properly described as a cure. It can only partly control the secondary consequences of the condition, which include kidney disease and thickening of the arteries. Nevertheless insulin is a drug of major importance and a life-saver for thousands of people.

Mixed blessings

The development of sulphonamides in the 1930s and of penicillin in the 1940s gave medicine greatly improved powers to control infection. Although by the 1940s TB was no longer the major killer it was in the nineteenth century, it has nevertheless been estimated that antibiotics have halved the number of deaths which might have been expected in the post-war period. Les Bennett is quick to point out that had it not been for streptomycin, he would have probably died from TB, as his father did. Antibiotics have helped make a whole range of other diseases, including bacterial pneumonia, childhood meningitis, gonorrhoea and syphilis, no longer killer illnesses. And they have ensured that far fewer people now die from infections following operations.

There is evidence, however, that antibiotics are over-used. For instance they are often prescribed for ear, nose and throat infections which are caused by viruses and thus cannot be helped by antibiotics, which only affect bacterial infections. Antibiotics also often cause thrush, diarrhoea and mood changes, particularly depression. They do not prevent the return of recurrent infections, to which many people are prone, including cystitis, sinusitis and sore throats, and there is some evidence that they may even make it more likely that infections return. Equally worrying, the over-use of antibiotics on whole populations can hasten the development of antibiotic-resistant bacteria. Thousands of people died in Mexico between 1972 and 1974 from a typhoid epidemic which was resistant to chloramphenicol, the only antibiotic effective in the treatment of typhoid, as a result of over-prescribing this potent and potentially toxic drug for non-life-threatening conditions.

When corticosteroids, powerful suppressors of the symptoms of inflammation and allergy, were first introduced in the 1950s, they were hailed as another wonder drug. They can be life-saving in conditions of severe shock. But they are also used in the treatment of non-life-threatening conditions, including rheumatic disorders and skin problems. The problem with steroids is that in suppressing inflammation, they also suppress the body's own defences, including immunity to infection. The possible effects include reduced resistance to infection, increases in blood pressure and weight, weakening of the bones and connective tissue, ulcers and mood changes, including severe depression. In children they can suppress growth. They should only be used in situations of such severity that their advantages outweigh their disadvantages. If used in chronic problems, particularly skin disorders, the problem returns once the treatment stops, and long-term treatment may make the condition worse. Shan, for instance, found her dermatitis became worse while she was using a steroid skin cream. Once she stopped using it and was no longer in contact with the factory chemicals, the problem cleared up.

Pregnancy and birth

Medical intervention in childbirth can be life-saving. Without caesarian operations many more mothers and babies would die. But there is little evidence to support the claim that it is primarily developments in obstetrics which have improved the perinatal mortality rate. The improvement is mainly a result of better living and working conditions, particularly improved maternal nutrition, and a smaller number of births among older women who have already had many children. Prompt intervention in childbirth can also be crucial in preventing handicap, particularly in ensuring that the baby is not brain-damaged by being starved of oxygen. But, sadly, the vast majority of handicaps are not caused by events around the time of birth. The mother's health in early pregnancy is a more crucial factor. It has been estimated that only 2 or 3 per cent of all handicapped children have disabilities related specifically to events in childbirth.[25]

Ultrasound scanning can be helpful in establishing whether it may be necessary to intervene in labour and in reassuring a woman who has previously had a malformed child that her baby is not damaged. Amniocentesis and the alphafetoprotein test give women at risk the option of an abortion if they are found to be carrying a handicapped child. But the effectiveness of many forms of new obstetric technology introduced in the 1970s has not been definitely established. Three out of four clinical trials of electronic foetal monitoring failed to find any advantage for the babies monitored electronically.[26] Although some caesarian operations are essential, some doctors carry out many more than others. Yet there is no evidence that the doctors who do a lot of caesarians can claim to have delivered fewer dead or handicapped babies, even when account is taken of the fact that they are likely to be dealing with a higher proportion of high-risk births.[27]

In addition, many of the new procedures in childbirth bring with them their own hazards. Electronic foetal monitoring prevents women adopting alternative postures for labour, despite evidence that lying down flat on your back leads to more complications and longer labours.[28] Intensive care units enable some premature babies who would otherwise have died to live. But there is a controversy about whether the growth of such units has increased the number of severely handicapped babies surviving. As for the continuing debate about whether home or hospital births are safer, the evidence remains contradictory. What can be said is that obstetricians have not yet produced any substantial body of evidence in support of their view that births in high-technology hospitals are obviously safer. In Holland, where many more babies are born at home, mortality rates are lower than in Britain.[29]

Preventive medicine?

If medicine cannot give us cures, it is argued, it could do more by acting earlier to prevent illness. If only the danger signs were recognized, the argument goes, if only we could catch it before it began, or in the early stages, we could head off illness with appropriate treatment. In Andrew Tree's factory this was the thinking behind the doctors' confidence in the value of medical check-ups. The workers, having seen many of their colleagues die, despite early diagnosis and treatment, were more sceptical.

Medicine's preventive activities fall into two categories: screening and immunization. Immunization was introduced at a time when improved conditions of life had reduced the prevalence of most infectious diseases and their likelihood of proving fatal. It is possible that these illnesses might have died out of their own accord without the introduction of immunization. The Netherlands had the lowest death rates from TB for any European country in the late 1950s and early 1960s despite not having a BCG programme. Levels of whooping cough have fallen in Germany, just as they did in Britain until very recently, although Germany has no whooping cough vaccination programme. Of the various vaccinations given for diseases found in Britain it seems that diphtheria and polio are the only ones whose effectiveness has definitely been established.[30] The case for whooping cough vaccination is already a matter for debate. It is estimated that each year twenty-five children are brain-damaged by the vaccination.[31] In 1980 there were six deaths from whooping cough.[32] The issues are complex: if no children were brain-damaged because vaccination was stopped, several hundred would die of the disease.

Three forms of screening are currently popular with doctors: blood pressure screening and screening for cervical cancer and breast cancer. The principle that prevention is better than cure is not in doubt. The problem is whether, once a medical need has been discovered, a treatment can be found which is effective and does not have adverse effects. What is on offer is not true prevention, but early diagnosis.

In the 1950s new drugs became available for dangerously raised blood pressure, a condition which, though symptomless, increases the risk of heart attacks, kidney failure and strokes. For people with very high blood pressure, taking these drugs has been shown to reduce particularly the likelihood of having a stroke. Some doctors, however, are already prescribing medication for all patients with even mildly raised blood pressure. The sales of blood pressure drugs doubled between 1975 and 1980. The problem is that, although you normally have to take them for the rest of your life, the drugs can cause drowsiness, impotence and depression.[33] It has been estimated that there are three million 'mild hypertensives' in Britain. Should all of them be put on drugs for the rest of their lives? Might there be other ways of reducing blood pressure? As the *British Medical Journal* commented: 'Are the benefits of treatment likely to be offset by an increase in the anxiety, distress and side effects as well as the cost of drug taking? Medicine which is good for the patient may not always be good for the person.'[34]

The effectiveness of breast screening, whether through self-examination or mammography, has also not been firmly established yet. It has been shown that where malignant lumps are removed early, women live three to four years longer after the operation. This may, however, simply be due to earlier detection rather than increased life expectancy.[35] The introduction of cervical screening has not made a major impact on the death rate from cervical cancer in Britain.[36] This may be because pre-cancerous cells found in the uterus do not necessarily turn into cancer, and therefore removing them may not help. Or it may be that screening is not reaching the women most at risk. It is true that in some parts of the world the cervical cancer death rate has fallen after intensive screening. Some people argue that death rates have also fallen in some areas without screening, indicating there may be other factors at work, while others believe that the reduction in death rates is evidence of the value of cervical screening.

We are also led to believe that it is a good preventive practice to go to the dentist every six months.[37] Tooth decay and gum disease can be prevented by careful brushing and cutting down on sugar,[38] but dental intervention does not necessarily save teeth. A government survey has shown that more teeth are healthy in adults who do not go to the dentist than among those who go regularly.[39] Although women are not more prone to dental disease than men, they are both more conscientious about going to the dentist *and* end up losing their teeth more often.[40] In children tooth decay is frequently reversible with changes in diet and use of fluoride, but filling teeth too early does not give time for the fluoride treatment to work.[41] In 95 per cent of fillings, the drill damages neighbouring teeth, making them more liable to decay as the hard outer layer is removed.[42] Once a tooth is filled it needs to be refilled, and each time this happens a bigger hole has to be drilled, weakening the tooth.[43] Increasingly, instead of advising patients about proper brushing and fluoride, dentists are persuading their patients to have 'preventive treatment', building up the myth that the answers lie in their – rather than our – hands.

Contraception

Doctors also put contraception in the category of 'preventive medicine', a strange place for it to be. The women's movement has made the risks and benefits of different forms of contraception perhaps better known than those of many other procedures supervised by doctors. After twenty years of the pill and the IUD, doubts about these methods are growing rather than receding. The pill trebles the risk of thrombosis in older women. But we also do not like some of the pill's more everyday effects, including nausea, lethargy and reduced sexual feelings. We are unhappy, too, about permanently taking a hormone drug which may also have an effect on our emotions. It is frightening to think that our feelings may be affected by the drugs we are taking. The IUD not only causes painful periods for many of its users but also carries a five-fold increase in the risk of infection, sterility and ectopic pregnancy in women who have not had children. Even among women who have had children these risks are doubled.

Like many other medical innovations, the pill and the IUD have not lived up to their initial promise. We were told we were entering the era of unproblematic contraception. There is still no contraceptive which does not have difficulties and drawbacks, and many women continue to be uneasy about their chosen form of birth control. The growing popularity of Depo-Provera, the injectable contraceptive, highlights the contradiction between our needs as women and what the pharmaceutical companies and some doctors see as good contraception. It is effective in preventing pregnancy, and the three-monthly injections ensure there can be no user error. Meanwhile its common side effects include weight gain, depression, lack of interest in sex, menstrual irregularities and delayed return of fertility. Research studies carried out by the manufacturers have also not been sufficiently rigorous to rule out the possibility that Depo-Provera may cause infertility and cancer.

Whose victory?

Medicine can help us, particularly if we are basically healthy, as when we have accidents or need a hernia repaired. But the vast growth of medical research has not brought with it the huge strides forward often claimed. Many of the medical interventions useful today, including surgical techniques, insulin and antibiotics, were developed before the big surge of activity in the last twenty years. The developments which have made a big difference to the length or quality of a significant number of people's lives in the past two decades can be counted on the fingers of one hand: the cure of maybe one per cent of cancers, hormone replacement therapy for a small group of people with endocrine problems, heart surgery for a small proportion of people at risk of heart attacks, the extension of life for people with kidney failure and more sophisticated surgical techniques.

Our sense of the power of medicine comes not only from what we hear of its present achievements but from what we are told of what it has done in the past. In particular our confidence that medicine will in time overcome the modern scourges is based on what we learn of its effectiveness in the earlier part of the twentieth century in conquering infectious disease. In less than half a century the disease pattern in our society has radically altered. Infectious diseases have moved from their position as the foremost cause of death to a residual category in the death statistics. To have brought about such a massive change through medication would indeed have been a major triumph for medicine. There is, however, little evidence that the decline of the infectious diseases can be attributed to medicine. The major reduction in deaths from the big killers of the nineteenth century, tuberculosis, bronchitis, pneumonia and influenza, cholera, diarrhoea, dysentery, typhoid, scarlet fever and diphtheria, took place *before* the introduction of modern medical treatments for these conditions.

Thomas McKeown, who was professor of social medicine at the University of Birmingham, demonstrates the relatively small contribution of medicine to the decline of the infectious diseases in his book *The Role of Medicine*.[44] The death rate from tuberculosis had already fallen to a tenth of the rate a hundred years before by the time streptomycin was introduced in the 1940s, shortly followed by the BCG vaccination in the early 1950s. Ninety-five per cent of the improvement in the death rate from cholera and other diarrhoeal diseases occurred before the introduction of intravenous treatment in the 1930s. Typhoid died out in Britain before the development of any form of treatment. The drug chloramphenicol was introduced to treat typhus and paratyphoid in 1950, but by that time these infections had almost disappeared in Britain. The death rate from scarlet fever and diphtheria had already been more than halved before diphtheria anti-toxin came into use at the end of the nineteenth century. The death rate from bronchitis, pneumonia and influenza has been falling steadily since the beginning of the twentieth century; the introduction of antibiotics in the 1940s did not speed up the rate at which the number of deaths was decreasing.

Great expectations

What has changed in the last twenty years is medicine's understanding of the biological processes of illness and the diagnostic equipment to establish these diagnoses. There is now a new understanding of the physiology of cancer, down to the genetic structure of the cancer cell. There have also been major changes in the understanding of how hormones control the immune mechanisms, of genetic engineering and of brain chemistry. There are whole new kinds of technology to assist in diagnosis, including computerized analysis of the blood and the whole body scanner. This machine is able to complement existing methods of diagnosing cancer in complicated cases with fewer unpleasant internal investigations. Encouraged by the manufacturers, hundreds of people have spent many hours raising charity money to buy the 'cancer scanner' for hospitals in the belief that it will save lives, but there is no evidence this is what it can do. As we have seen, accurate diagnosis does not necessarily mean the cancer can be dealt with, even if it is at an early stage. The tragic fallacy of medicine is that it is assumed that diagnosis – the knowledge of the biology, microbiology and physiology of a disorder – makes cure possible. But it is becoming increasingly clear that the jump from physiological knowledge to effective treatment can rarely be easily made.

Sometimes it is said that the problem with medicine is its 'high technology'. This view confuses two separate criticisms of medicine. The first is that there is a dynamic within medicine which draws resources into sophisticated medical procedures. The second is that there is something intrinsically better about primary care – clinics, health centres and GPs' surgeries – than hospital medicine. There is ample evidence to support the first view. As we will discuss in the next chapter, resources are found far more easily for technological innovations than for district nurses or locally based physiotherapists. There is also no doubt that pharmaceutical and medical equipment companies shape the direction in which developments take place, and doctors fail to resist this pressure. On the second point the evidence is less clear-cut. A lot of what medicine does best is in the medium technology field, coping with accidents and emergencies and undertaking routine surgery. And there are very sophisticated procedures – like hip replacement – which are of certain benefit. Vera Mitchell, while highly critical of medicine in many ways, insists: 'My life has been saved two or three times by the fact that there is a National Health Service and very expensive treatment is readily available. The drug heparin, for instance, was used to contain a clot. We have not got to lose sight of that.'

A rigid view which says 'high technology' is bad while primary care is good fails to acknowledge the extent to which a common philosophy pervades medical practice at all levels. Our disappointment and distress come from procedures becoming widely used before they have been properly evaluated and the over-use of treatment in circumstances where it is not appropriate. Both happen at all levels. It is the same way of thinking which leads to the automatic prescription of blood pressure drugs in cases of mild hypertension and to the over-use of cytotoxic drugs in cancer. It is a desire to do something rather than nothing and a failure to look at the consequences of clinical intervention for the quality of people's lives.

Medicine is not useless in the treatment of common illnesses, and there have been many helpful advances in the last twenty or thirty years. But what it can do is often very much less than what we have been led to believe it can do. It does not have the answer to the majority of everyday health problems. Although it can relieve symptoms – sometimes very effectively and sometimes less effectively – it cannot give us health. Medicine cannot be blamed for developing procedures with contradictory consequences. The harm is less in the techniques themselves than in medicine's own claims for itself. In learned conferences doctors may share their doubts with each other, but these rarely reach the outside world. And so we accept what medicine offers us on its terms. The message is that medicine can cure us. The myth is so powerful that we tend to overlook the evidence – not just from research, but from our own lives – that its achievements are very much more modest.

6 The Subjugation of Care

When we think of the health service we usually think of hospitals. In our heads most of us carry an 'Emergency Ward Ten' view of what they are like. We are ill. We submit to firm hands and sweet smiles and go home cured. Illness is followed by medical intervention (usually an operation, but sometimes other procedures which are rather hazier in our imaginations) and then we are better. In our imaginary ward, people of assorted ages lie propped up by starched white pillows, surrounded by fruit and flowers. Although their conversation is still languid, their cheerful smiles testify to growing strength and vigour.[1]

This is the reality for some people, especially if they are under forty-five and have had an accident or a routine operation. But the way we imagine what happens only applies to a minority of people. The majority of hospital beds are not filled with people there to be cured. Over half the NHS's hospital beds[2] are in hospitals for elderly people, for mentally handicapped people and people with psychiatric illness, the vast majority of whom will never leave. In general hospitals the picture is not as different as we might expect. A minority of people can expect to get fully better. Although the Department of Health calls them 'acute' hospitals, this is really a misnomer. The orthopaedic wards, where people recover from broken bones, are partly as we imagine them. But the average general medical ward comes as a shock. One in two people is elderly. Some may also be psychiatrically disturbed. Many are there in a severe phase of a recurrent condition, like asthma or emphysema. Others have had strokes or heart attacks. They can expect rehabilitation but not cure. More surgical patients do get fully better, but a proportion have cancer, and for most of these surgery will be palliative rather than curative.

Most people are in hospital to be cared for rather than cured. Hospital workers look after us when we are too weak to look after ourselves; they reassure us, feed us, keep us clean, relieve our pain, help us to live with our disabilities and to resume everyday life. Medical intervention is only a part of what goes on. Speech therapists, dieticians, physiotherapists, occupational therapists, nurses and ancillary workers all make a different contribution to our care and recovery.

But although we may have got our picture of what goes on in hospitals wrong, we should not feel we are ignorant outsiders who have fallen for a stereotype. The view that we as lay people have picked up of what hospitals are all about is also the dominant view inside them. Hospitals are organized on the assumption that diagnosis and clinical intervention are the primary activities and that other aspects of hospital work, including care and rehabilitation, are subordinate.

Clinical supremacy

The domination of health care by internal investigation and treatment and those who practise them takes place at a number of levels.

Although health care involves a range of skills, medicine carries the greatest prestige. It also attempts to shape and dominate the way other health workers are trained and carry out their work. Midwives, for instance, point to medicine's erosion of their skills and autonomy. From the level of government decisions about how much should be spent on what in the NHS down to the care of individual patients, the doctors' view tends to prevail. Medicine has established the principle that clinical judgement is unquestionable, and this powerful notion dominates all kinds of health service activity.

But it is not just that doctors and the institution of medicine dominate other groups of workers who have other skills. It is also that within medicine, diagnosis and clinical intervention are both the primary focus of doctors' education and a key to their prestige. In medical schools students are taught anatomy, physiology and biochemistry. A lot of time is spent learning to diagnose relatively uncommon conditions. Most medical students spend only a few weeks outside the hospital looking at health and illness in the environment where it is produced and seeing the conditions in which people recuperate once discharged from hospital. Despite the large numbers of elderly people among the sick, very little time is spent looking at their special needs or on good practice in rehabilitation. Medical students are taught to prescribe 't.l.c.' – tender loving care – as a last resort when there is no other possible form of treatment. Nursing training does not challenge this belittlement of nursing skills. Nurses, too, are taught according to medicine's priorities.

Within medical practice it is diagnosis and internal intervention which carry the greatest fascination. A middle-aged man has a rare neurological condition. The nurses observe that every day several doctors come to visit him. They earnestly discuss his condition. Medical students come too. They huddle round the bed absorbing information about the man's interesting case. The doctors agree to operate. During the operation the man suffers a stroke and he emerges paralysed down one side. His speech is slurred and he cannot be easily understood. Only slow painstaking rehabilitation will help him back to half normal life. He is no longer the subject of medical interest; the doctors hurry past this testament to their failure. On the ward round they stop for barely half a minute: 'And how are you today?' Before he has had time to absorb the question and begin to express his reply, the doctors and students have passed on.

Within medicine there is a curious hierarchy of specialisms. In general the consultants working in medicine's most esoteric areas, where there is maximum scope for sophisticated diagnosis and intervention, are the most revered. In areas like neurology, neurosurgery, cardiology and gastroenterology, jobs are most highly sought after, merit awards (additional payments from the NHS to selected consultants) are most often given and consultants occupy the most powerful committee positions. General surgery has an intermediate position, followed by general medicine. Specialisms in sexually transmitted diseases, accident and emergency and psychiatry carry less status. At the bottom of the pile come geriatrics and mental handicap. It is no coincidence that doctors who are women or black are most often to be found working in these latter specialities. The ranking may reflect opportunities for spectacular, if rare, cures or for private practice. It is certainly not necessarily related to possibilities for effective treatment or opportunities for improving the quality of people's lives. It is illnesses which present the greatest complexity of investigation and intervention that carry the greatest prestige.

Thomas McKeown, who highlighted the limitations of medicine's capacity to cure, argues that the assumption that disease can be dealt with primarily by internal intervention has led to the 'relative neglect of the majority of people who provide no scope for the internal measures which are at the centre of medical interest.'[3] In addition, medicine's preoccupation with ever more sophisticated diagnosis and treatment means that the more routine procedures it could do so well, such as the everyday operations for which there are long waiting lists, do not attract prestige or resources. The low status of those aspects of health service work which are to do with caring rather than attempts to cure, and the high status of activities with large scope for internal investigation and intervention have profound effects on how money is spent in the NHS. It also influences how health care is organized, how services are developed and under-developed, and our experience as patients.

Medicine may not offer so many cures as we imagine, but there is much hospitals can do and could do much better in terms of everyday health *care*. To understand how these health care needs get lost, however, we need to look not just at the medical hierarchy, but at a second power structure. The way health care is organized and how money gets spent is, of course, not directly the province of doctors, but of the NHS management system. Treasurers and administrators have different preoccupations from doctors. They have to balance the books; their primary concern is with efficiency and value for money. Both the medical hierarchy and the management hierarchy are represented in the Department of Health and in regional and district management teams. They have different values and priorities, but their interaction shapes the health care system. Health workers and patients are subject to both power structures.

Factory values

The hospital of concrete and glass is newly built. Like many hospitals it has a subterranean private life. Beneath the semi-public world of wards, operating theatres and laboratories, other staff work underground in the sterile supplies unit, stores and kitchens. In this hospital, as in older hospitals, the endless corridors of the upper regions are mirrored in a network of basement tunnels.

They have put a laundry in the basement too. At its centre is a windowless wash house. The laundry manager boasts the most up-to-date equipment. Temperatures are normally in the eighties or nineties. On the wall there is a chart showing the week's production. The number of sheets, pillow-cases and pyjamas washed each week is carefully recorded. How much the staff are paid depends on how many items are washed. To make a living wage you cannot afford to slow down the pace of work. Those who wash the foul linen get an extra 80p a day. The staff are bitter. The new hospital has many official visitors, but none come down here.

The laundry is run on factory principles, like the rest of the hospital. Efficiency and rationalization are watchwords. There used to be a domestic attached to every ward. She used to know everybody – the pleasure of the work was talking to the patients. Now that they have reduced the number of domestics, she must clean wherever she is sent. Each day she goes to three or four different wards. It is more exhausting, more monotonous, less rewarding. Here, as in the factories described by Shan, George, Baden and Andrew, workers' needs are subordinated to productivity. Having health as its official purpose does not make the hospital a kinder working environment. To pay the rent and save up for holidays, you have to work long and unsocial hours. To get fewer people to do more work, bonus schemes have been introduced. The pastry-cooks used to make Danish pastries and fancy cakes for the patients, but since the bonus scheme they have given it up. What you get paid depends on quantity, not quality. Porters and operating department assistants make up their incomes by long hours of overtime. The personnel manager would like to devise a scheme to cut overtime. If it were not for the union he would have cut hours and increased the workload long ago.

The system for organizing hospital work is modelled on the industrial management system. Just like factories, hospitals have a sophisticated management system. There are domestic managers, works managers, nurse managers and personnel managers. At the bottom of each management hierarchy, the work of junior managers is routine and not highly paid. But those who wish to reach the top must demonstrate zeal for cost-cutting and efficiency, even if it is at the expense of health workers' living standards or conditions of work. The aim of the hospital management system is the same as the factory management system, to get more work done for less money. Just like the factory managers, District Management Teams constantly devise new schemes to improve productivity and output.

These initiatives affect the nurses, lab staff and operating technicians, as well as the ancillary workers, porters, cooks and cleaners. Obviously, ideas for better organization should in principle be welcome, but the aim of the management system is to up the workload – whether this is the number of patients on a ward, the number of samples analysed or the number of operations carried out – while at the same time keeping staffing levels constant or reducing them. As a result the staff get busier and busier. It is no wonder that hospital managers complain of rocketing sickness absence rates, particularly among nurses – or that the General Nursing Council reports more and more nurses coming before disciplinary hearings for errors caused by pressure of work.

Here is how one nurse, working on the night shift at a prestigious London postgraduate hospital, described the pressures on her:

My take-home wage is bad, but all of us get so tired. Mentally it is very tense. At my hospital ancillary workers are paid double for nights, but we only get an extra 10p an hour. So they have cut down on ancillary staff, because nurses are cheaper. We have to do the washing up. It sounds nothing, but if you have got a cardiac arrest and you are thinking about the washing up, it is too much. The other night there was no porter. Nurses had to take a patient to the morgue, because the cost of employing a night porter is more than employing a nurse. The work is becoming more stressful too, because the patients are becoming increasingly violent. If they have had to wait five or six hours in casualty the patients get very aggressive. I don't know of another job where a person comes home so shattered.[4]

Practices and values from business management pervade the hospital at all levels. They are there on the shop floor, in the wards, kitchens and laboratories, but they are also present at the level of policy-making. The present framework of health service planning and organization was devised with the help of McKinsey and Co., Inc., a team of American consultants who pioneered new management methods in British industry during the 1960s. They were commissioned by the Conservative government which came into office in 1970, and their proposals were carried out by the Labour government's implementation of the NHS reorganization in 1974.[5] Recently a team of top British

businessmen, headed by Mr Roy Griffiths, Deputy Chairman
and Managing Director of Sainsburys, have been brought in by
the Secretary of State to advise on ways of getting better 'value
for money' in the NHS.[6]

Work under medicine

What makes the experience of health workers different from that
of factory workers is that their work is shaped not only by the
industrial management system but by the medical hierarchy.
When nurses and other health workers talk of the difficulties and
frustrations they face, they tell of long hours, exhausting work-
loads, staff and resource shortages, and they also describe how
they feel their work is undermined by medical values.

It is hard for outsiders to understand health workers' feelings
about doctors. The consultant is not accountable to anyone. He
can be late for his ward round or his outpatients clinic because
he has been seeing his private patients, but he need not apologize.
He can keep his waiting list under lock and key without scrutiny
from anyone else. He may be admitting his own private patients
as NHS patients, but no one has the right to challenge him. In
most hospitals he can spend what he likes on drugs, while the
books are balanced by cuts under other budget headings, like
cleaning or catering.

Yet health workers' resentment extends beyond the idiosyn-
crasies of the consultants to the way medical values dominate the
rest of hospital practice. The elderly man is thin and jaundiced.
He is in pain. He has a carcinoma at the head of the pancreas.
An exploratory operation has revealed that he is riddled with
cancer. The doctors are keeping him alive by draining off fluid
through a tube in the side of his body. No one has openly told
him he is dying, although the nurses know he knows. Every day
for weeks the man has said 'Why the tube? I want it taken away.'
Sometimes he tries to pull it out. Knowing he will die, the nurses
keep telling him 'The tube will make you better.' Privately, the

nurses understand and sympathize with the man's wish to die. But the nurses have not felt able to tell the doctors this, and the doctors have not asked. There has been no discussion between the doctors and the nurses or with the man and his family about whether it is appropriate to prolong his life for a few more agonizing weeks.

The junior nurse or domestic, because she has more frequent and friendly contact with individual patients, often knows the ill person better than anyone in the hospital. Yet it would be almost unthinkable for the junior or auxiliary nurse to speak to the doctor of what she has learned and even less to play a role in discussing the person's care. Those who are most involved have the least say. So knowledge of some of the patients' needs, like unhappiness with a particular treatment, tends not to get fed back to doctors. The rigid hierarchy permits little questioning, discussion or mutual learning. More senior nurses do discuss the patients with doctors, but they are not expected to question the doctors' judgement. The care nurses provide is seen as supplementary to medicine. It is rarely acknowledged that the course of treatment of an ill person is a matter in which nurses should have a central say. In any case, nurses tend not to express their view explicitly, because it takes a lot of confidence for women of low status to confront men of high class and status, and they have not the formal right to challenge the doctor's clinical judgement. What often happens in practice is that instead of the conflict and resentment being expressed openly, the nurses quietly disobey the doctors' instructions. Each consultant may have a different view on the kind of bowel wash-out to be carried out before an operation, but on a busy morning the nurses do them all the same way. The doctor may prescribe a laxative, but if the nurse thinks it is inappropriate she may 'forget' to give it. The effect of this undercover subversion, however, is that there is no dynamic for change, and the relative powerlessness of nurses continues.

Although the nurse's job is to do with care rather than treatment, nursing training still very much reflects medicine's priorities. Without denying the importance of post-operative care, for instance, the emphasis is very much on the clinical side, rather than on rehabilitation or the special needs of the elderly. Nurses complain that outside the hospital their skills are romanticized, but inside they are undervalued. The contribution of nursing to healing is underestimated. Caring and looking after people are seen as a residual activity, strictly subordinate to medicine. Other health workers face similar problems. The physiotherapist has developed useful techniques for the relief of back pain, but the orthopaedic surgeon insists the physiotherapist must do it his way. The physiotherapist knows the orthopaedic surgeon's method is less effective, but cannot challenge his clinical judgement.

The nurse keeps her or his place and rarely questions the doctor. Nurses who have contested medicine's authority, for instance by refusing to carry out electroconvulsive therapy (a treatment for depression which often leaves people shocked and aching, and can cause loss of memory), have been sacked.[7]

Patient as product

It is to this world of factory values and medical hierarchies that the sick person comes. It is a world which is not separate from the social processes and forces which destroy our health, but a microcosm of it.

Inside the hospital both power structures bear on the patient. For the industrial management system the patient is the product. A central equation governs hospital management theory:

$$\frac{\text{annual deaths and discharges}}{\text{available beds}} = \text{throughput}$$

The ambitious senior hospital manager confides 'We've upped the throughput, you know.' Throughput is a measure of the speed at which sick people pass through hospital. There is no other index of hospital efficiency. Hospitals with low throughput invite the attention of health authorities as possible candidates for closure. Among all the statistics routinely compiled by British hospitals and collected by the government, there is not one which reflects whether the patients get better or worse. Indeed, for statistical purposes it does not matter whether the patient comes out dead or alive, as deaths are not distinguished from discharges.

To achieve high throughput the hospital manager must ensure that the maximum number of people pass through the minimum number of beds in the shortest possible time.[8] Just as the good factory manager ensures he has no unused productive capacity, the good hospital manager keeps his beds as full as possible, to ensure that staff are used with maximum efficiency. He must not let his bed occupancy ratio fall. And just as the most profitable factory is the one which gets its workers to produce its products in the shortest possible time, so the efficient hospital manager tries to ensure that his patients spend the minimum time in hospital. Just as the factory manager cuts costs by rationalization, the hospital manager slims down his operation by cutting beds, getting rid of smaller hospitals and convalescent homes. With fewer beds there is greater pressure on doctors to discharge their patients earlier. Just as the factory manager improves profits by speeding up the production line, hospital managers seek greater 'intensity of use' of their beds. The costs in terms of overworked staff and premature discharge do not figure in the calculations.

The new policies mean the ward is fuller and the patients iller than they used to be. The staff are run off their feet. Six nurses cope with twenty-six patients, where they would once have had twenty. There is not time to listen to the ill people. No time to sit and hold someone's hand when they come round from an operation. No time to take a break.

The discharged patients suffer too. An elderly man has bronchitis. At home he must skimp on fuel, so his house is never warm, and he lives alone. In the hospital he needs little more than rest and food, but he needs these very badly. The consultant says the beds are needed for people having specific medical treatment, so he must go home. A middle-aged woman has had a hysterectomy. She is shocked and in pain. At home there will be no rest. She must start looking after her three children straight away. She needs to convalesce, but the convalescent home has been closed and the pressure on beds is too great to keep her in any longer.

In the winter the pressure on beds and staff is worse. Norms calculated on average bed occupancy do not take account of winter flu epidemics, hypothermia and pneumonia. Many hospitals are full to bursting. A few years ago hospitals short of beds used to cope by closing their doors to emergencies. But this proved embarrassing when nearby hospitals were also closed. Now the instruction has come from Regional Health Authorities not to close to emergencies. Instead routine operations are cancelled (often patients may have their bags packed two or three times before they are finally admitted, and they may be called in at a moment's notice without having had time to make arrangements with their families). The administrators press the doctors to send their patients home early[9] and search the wards for undeclared empty beds. Patients can wait in Casualty for five or six hours before a bed can be found.

Ruth experienced both the hospital's factory values and the difficulties of coping at home after what she would argue was premature discharge:

While I was in hospital I did a survey. There were nineteen beds in my ward, and the ages of the women ranged from twenty-five to forty. They were all having their wombs out. They had an intake on Wednesday and they operated on Thursday, and then they had another intake on Monday and operated on Tuesday. It was like a conveyor belt. I still could not walk and was mentally distressed. They said I should rest when I got home, because I would get a hernia or something, but I said 'How am I going to rest in a half built house with men working everywhere in it?'

My daughter was meant to come and pick me up at ten in the morning, which means I was dressed from seven o'clock. Somebody had my bed at eleven o'clock, so I had no bed to lie down on. I was sitting in a chair and when the nurses wanted that chair, they moved me into another chair. And although I have every respect for the nurses, they kept pushing me around from chair to chair. They kept saying 'Mrs Hutchinson, aren't you going home?' 'What time are you going, Mrs Hutchinson?' And the doctors would come along and say 'I see you like staying here, Mrs Hutchinson!' And it just went on and on, and then I would go into the bathroom and cry. I said 'Please can't you take me home by ambulance?' But they said 'Well, it costs £40 to go home from here by ambulance, and you have to book it forty-eight hours in advance.'

In the hospital Ruth asked to be taken to a convalescent home and was refused. There was a time when women who had had hysterectomies were routinely sent to convalescent homes. But these days convalescence is seen as a luxury the NHS cannot afford. Many convalescent homes run by the health service have been closed and contracts with private or charitable homes discontinued. Part of the rationale for phasing convalescence out is that studies have shown that post-operative rehabilitation is not of *medical* benefit.[10]

Dual power

Although the hospital management system and the medical hierarchy often come into conflict (a go-ahead district administrator will complain that a particular consultant keeps his patients in the hospital twice as long as the other consultants), in general the values of the hospital management system compound rather than counter-balance medicine's clinical preoccupations. Senior administrators know that they can improve a hospital's intensity of use by squeezing convalescence and rehabilitation, because most senior doctors are preoccupied with other things.

When it comes to how money is spent in the NHS, the

hospital management system's concern to balance the books combines with medicine's emphasis on diagnosis and clinical intervention to reproduce a pattern of resource allocation in which everyday care is neglected. The stroke patient is an example of the kind of problem neither power structure welcomes. Although strokes are one of the most common reasons for hospital admission, it is often particularly difficult to find a bed for someone who has had a stroke. Stroke patients take a long time to get better. Sometimes they do not get better and have to stay permanently in hospital. Physiotherapy, speech therapy and occupational therapy can be very helpful, but there is little doctors can do. For medicine the stroke patient epitomizes 'the crumble', medical slang for the vast group of people who are medically uninteresting and for whom medicine cannot do very much. For the hospital manager the stroke patient is a classic bed blocker. 'Bed blockers' are usually elderly and occupy acute hospital beds for long periods, reducing throughput. They are numerous, expensive and unprestigious. How to get rid of them is a major subject of study in hospital management theory.[11]

Within the NHS there is a dynamic which draws resources into clinical intervention without passing through any formal decision-making process. The principle that doctors' clinical judgement cannot be questioned extends far beyond the bedside. The District Management Team – determines the budget for nursing and every other aspect of hospital life, but they do not have the right to limit what individual doctors spend. This comes within the area of direct clinical authority. If drug prices rise, or new and expensive treatments are introduced, the hospital administrators often end up reducing other services to compensate. Handing over Tadworth Court, a part of the Great Ormond Street Hospital for sick children, specializing in rehabilitation and long-term care, to charity, Norman Fowler, the then Secretary of State for Social Services, illustrated exactly this point. The NHS could no longer afford Tadworth Court, he explained, because of the ever-increasing cost of the high technology part of the hospital. New methods of treating malignant disease, the diagnosis and treatment of renal disease and the development of new surgical techniques had led to over-spending.[12] The Department of Health[13] clearly regards medical developments as unquestionably having the first call on resources and care, and convalescence as secondary. In taking this view, however, it is sanctioning an informal and *de facto* way of determining priorities which never comes before any formal decision-making body.

As well as having enormous informal power, senior consultants hold sway in the formal decision-making bodies too. Each health authority includes at least three doctors among its members. The District Management Team want to close the casualty department of a small hospital. The issue has split the health authority down the middle. The two hospital consultants back the DMT. The GP backs local people. During the debate the consultants read medical journals. The chairwoman has the casting vote and supports the closure. 'I voted with the doctors,' she explains.

How money gets spent follows the hierarchy of medical specialisms. This is partly because the most powerful doctors are in a position to press their case for resources most strongly. But it is also that spending on sophisticated medical equipment fits in with the hospital management system's productivity-oriented philosophy. The administrators' rationale for the purchase of much modern medical equipment is not so much that it is likely to improve clinical outcome as that it cuts the time spent by patients in hospitals and thus improves efficiency. One argument for laser surgery in the case of pre-cancerous changes in the cervix is that it can be done on an outpatient basis, cutting costs. The whole body scanner can also be used without admitting patients into hospital. Of course there are advantages for the patient; both procedures are much less uncomfortable than their predecessors. Balanced against this, however, is the problem that neither piece of equipment, while being very expensive, has definitely been shown to save or prolong the lives of cancer sufferers, for the reasons we discussed in the last chapter.

In contrast, spending on the long-stay hospitals and community services has few powerful advocates. Most districts have only one consultant in geriatrics and in mental handicap, while having dozens in the clinical specialties, so there are few doctors in a position to argue that money should be spent on the less prestigious parts of the health service. Hospital managers do pay lip service to the need to develop what are referred to, rather inappropriately, as 'the priority services'. But, for them, spending money on improving the quality of care pays few dividends in terms of balancing the books. There are exceptions. Spending money on psychiatric community nurses enables people to be given their injections at home rather than in hospital, facilitating what is called 'the management of the patient in the community'. Spending money on geriatric and psychiatric day hospitals cuts in-patient costs. But, for the most part, spending money on the geriatric, psychiatric and mental handicap hospitals or on community nurses and clinics feels like pouring money into a bottomless pit. The buildings are so dilapidated and the staffing ratios so poor that to have any impact millions and millions would have to be spent. In the long-stay hospitals even the food is of an inferior quality. On average nearly 40 per cent more is spent on each patient's meal in district general hospitals than in mental handicap hospitals.[14] Overall, although over 52 per cent of the NHS beds are in mental handicap, geriatric and mental illness hospitals, only 21 per cent of the health service's hospital budget is spent on them.[15]

The wastelands

The workhouses and asylums of the nineteenth century are now the home of hundreds of thousands of elderly, mentally ill and mentally handicapped people. Bleak, neglected and often difficult to get to, these are the wastelands of the NHS. They are monuments not just to medicine's inability to cure but also to its insistence that it must stay in control, whether or not it has got the answers.

Of course it is not quite as bad as the shocking documentaries on television. The administrator is pleased to report that the geriatric ward has just been upgraded. They have installed a hoist to make bathing easier and changed the lavatories so that you can get a wheelchair in and shut the door. There's a new day room too. Red high-backed plastic chairs round three walls, a potted plant and a television. The wards – twelve beds down each wall – have been repainted, and there is a brand-new identical locker by each bed. But there is no privacy, no activities other than the television and an occasional visit from a clergyman, no conversation. No one has found a way of overcoming the stench of incontinence.

Whether you like it or not, you still have to go to bed at three in the afternoon because they have cut back the staff on the evening shift. Tea is served in bed. If you were to have it later the hospital would have to pay the catering staff for unsocial hours.

In the mental handicap hospital the staff on one ward have clubbed together to re-wallpaper. With the Christmas money of the ward's thirty residents they have bought them each a purple nylon bedspread. The beds are tightly packed together with a row down the middle as well as at each side, but on each woman's locker they have stuck her photo. This is a 'high-grade' ward. The women can wash and feed themselves.

On the 'low-grade' ward all fourteen men are doubly in-continent. Half are in wheelchairs. The room where they spend their days has little furniture. The window has been broken and is temporarily boarded up. Those in wheelchairs sit in a row in front of the TV high up on the wall where it will not get broken. The others wander around aimlessly, shouting and reaching out to the occasional visitor. At bedtimes there are only two nurses to wash all fourteen men and put them to bed.

In the psychiatric hospital the Victorian heating system is failing. In some wards the temperature falls below 50° in the winter. Replacing it will cost half a million pounds, and the hospital just has not got that kind of money. They have managed a 'personalized clothing' scheme for the women patients. Now instead of being dressed in whatever comes out of the cupboard, each woman has been given three crimplene dresses of her own. Not that the scheme extends to underwear, not yet – that would mean extra laundry staff. Getting hot meals to the wards spread over the extensive grounds is a problem too. They are not as hot as they might be. In the next five-year plan the hospital is hoping for the money to install food-reheating equipment on each ward. But at the moment things look bleak. The catering budget is severely stretched. It is only possible to have cooked puddings for supper every other day.

In the daytime the psychiatric patients can go to an industrial training unit where they do packing for private companies. And there's a furniture workshop, an occupational therapy centre and one art therapist for over a thousand people. The day rooms of the long-stay ward have carpets and a few ornaments. But there are no homely comforts in the short-stay wards. The pale green paint is flaking from the walls. In a cavernous room there is a single ping-pong table and faded posters of the pop heroes of three years ago. In the room with easy chairs and the television there are no curtains or carpets. There is no private space. The charge nurse whispers 'We do not want to make it too comfortable, or they would all want to stay.'

Although in these hospitals most long-stay patients' actual contact with doctors is minimal (some people do not see their consultant from one year to the next), daily life is shaped by medicine's values and ways of thinking.[16] People are defined not by who they are but what is wrong or missing – 'schizophrenia', 'Down's syndrome', 'Parkinson's disease'. Their bedrooms are wards; their living rooms are day rooms. The NHS acknowledges its obligation to feed and clothe people, to keep them clean and to administer their medication. But, although throughout the long-stay hospitals individual health workers strive against impossible odds to improve the quality of life, the hospitals as institutions do not acknowledge an obligation to meet other human needs. The need for personal space, for friendship, for identity. The people who must live in the NHS's long-term hospitals exist in a hollowed-out world. Medicine insists they come under its jurisdiction and yet it has no answers to their problems. Their lives are at the same time defined by and abandoned by medicine.

Our everyday needs

It is often said that too much money is spent on the 'acute' sector, while the community services and long-stay hospitals are deprived of resources. But although it is true that there is a grave imbalance between the sectors, this is not quite right. Much of what happens in general hospitals is routine and equally undervalued too. And when there is pressure on resources, as we have shown, it is the everyday quality of care, rather than sophisticated medical intervention, which suffers. Those who defend a small general hospital against closure are sometimes accused of preventing the march of progress and the transfer of resources to the long-stay and community sectors. In fact what is usually happening is that acute services are being rationalized, centralized and intensified, but no less is being spent on them. The bigger hospital we must now go to is further away, harder to get to, less interested in minor problems and provides less personal care. To defend resources in the acute sector is to defend routine care.

Health care is not just about helping people get better; it is also about the quality of the experience of illness. Good everyday health care is the home nurse arriving at the time she said she would, not half a day later. It is about having operations when you need them, not six months afterwards. It's about health workers with time to listen to your worries and to explain what is happening. It is about being able to get the batteries on your hearing aid renewed. It is about being looked after near enough home to enable your relatives to visit when they want. It is about getting your delivery of incontinence pads before the last lot run out, getting the right size and having somewhere to dispose of them. It is about someone recognizing that you will not get better if there is no one to go to the shops for you or to cook you a hot meal. It is about continuing to see sick people as having normal human needs rather than as an extension of their disease, and remembering that healing must involve meeting these needs.

At present there are few among those who determine how money is spent and how health care is organized who are in touch with these needs and who see meeting them as the cornerstone of health care. As a result, what health care could do best, our hospitals do worst. Throughout the health service there are thousands of health workers, nurses, occupational therapists, auxiliary staff, physiotherapists, dieticians, cooks and doctors with ideas about how the caring work of the NHS could be improved and struggling to put them into practice. But within the medical/managerial power structure, everyday health care has few powerful defenders.

7 Intimate Encounters

When we grumble about the health service we tell each other of long waits to see about a minor operation, of the difficulty of getting help at home for a sick elderly relative, or of having to take a child with a minor injury on a difficult bus journey to get to the nearest Casualty. But our complaints go beyond the problems of an under-financed NHS which puts its money into sophisticated diagnosis and treatment at the expense of everyday care: 'The doctor starts writing on his pad before you sit down' ... 'When I get out of the surgery I remember all the questions I wanted to ask' ... 'I was telling him about the pains in my chest, how they come and go at certain times of the day, but he cut me off' ... 'He didn't seem interested' ... 'She said it's all psychological and gave me some Valium' ... 'The doctor says I am over-anxious about the kids, but if I didn't call him and something awful happened I know he'd blame me for neglecting them' ... 'He never listens really. You go back again and again with the same problems' ... 'I tried to tell him how the tablets make me feel sick and giddy, but he ignored me. I ended up flushing them down the toilet' ... 'She couldn't find anything wrong. She implied I was neurotic.'

Some people speak highly of their doctors. A few doctors have the respect and affection of the majority of their patients. But a visit to a pensioners' club, a mother-and-toddlers club or a chat with friends or workmates reveals a remarkably consistent picture. Many, many people express feelings which range from discomfort to distress when talking about their doctors.

Of course people's feelings about their doctors are often very mixed. Sometimes deep gratitude and resentment or distress are expressed almost in the same breath, especially if the person has been seriously ill. It is not uncommon for people to begin 'Of course the doctors were wonderful' and then go on to describe an experience which was upsetting or made them angry. Most of us desperately want to have confidence in our doctors.

Doctors grumble about their patients too: 'They are mainly unemployed. They come with "de pain in de head". What am I meant to do about it?' . . . 'All they want is a prescription and won't go away until you give them one' . . . 'She's schizophrenic, you know' . . . 'I can't understand why they won't go to the clinic. Aren't they proud of their babies?' . . . 'You tell them it will kill them if they don't lose weight, but they don't take any notice' . . . 'All my social class one and two patients have cut down on smoking, but it is impossible to get through to class four and five.'

Our perceptions as patients are not a figment of our imaginations. The disdain, incomprehension and sometimes hostility we perceive reflects attitudes which are widespread among doctors. In this chapter we explore some of the themes which recur when we tell each other about our encounters with doctors. Most people – women, black people, elderly people, working-class people – will recognize them. Readers who share the doctors' status and social world, especially if they are men, may have to exercise their imaginations. The intimate encounter is also usually a class encounter, and it is qualitatively different for the small minority of people whom the doctor sees as more or less an equal.

The difficulties we complain of are of course rooted in real constraints on the doctor. He or she is short of time, and our problems are often overwhelming. But in some ways these constraints are also self-inflicted. Since the inception of the NHS, general practitioners have fought to retain their independence from the government. They have insisted they do not want to be state employees. As 'independent contractors' they receive a fee from the government for every patient on their list, plus additional money if the patient is elderly or if additional services such as family planning are rendered. To keep up their earnings, the more patients GPs have, the better. Although there are grants and subsidies for additional staff, premises and equipment, GPs must pay out of their own pockets to develop their work. Being a successful GP requires careful financial management to get the most out of the government. The magazines available to GPs advise on the best strategies.[1] When the doctors' surgeries are run down, they appear pressed for time and their waiting rooms are full, it is the fiercely defended choice of their profession that things are this way.

The besieged

One window of the health centre has been boarded up. Dwarfed by the giant tower blocks, the single-storey building seems as insubstantial as a matchbox. Inside, the waiting room is almost full. On the wall a handwritten notice demands that all prams are left outside.

Usually it takes four days to get an appointment. As the telephones on the outlying parts of the estate are often broken, you can end up making two trips to see the GP. For the man with chronic arthritis who lives in an old terrace house beyond the estate, arranging to see the doctor is in itself a nightmare. Local people complain that the health centre doctors have refused to take on any more council tenants: 'They say they cannot find the flats in the dark.' The health centre has also told pensioners who have recently moved into the new bungalows that they must go elsewhere. Some people with mental health problems, needing a lot of the doctors' time, have been put off the doctors' lists. They tour the local surgeries. No GP wants another's rejects.

The senior doctor holds a key position on the local Family Practitioner Committee. As he describes how he runs his practice, he chain-smokes small cigars. A competent doctor can cope with 3,500 patients, he says – nearly twice the norm. The more patients, the higher his earnings. The delay in getting an appointment is a problem, he admits. When he is short-staffed it is true that patients sometimes have to wait ten days. A good practice should be able to see people within three or four days. He is proud of how many patients he can see in an hour. He has conducted his own efficiency study: he sees eleven people an hour on average; his partner, ten. As for putting patients off his list, he only does it occasionally, with difficult patients. The doctor is free to choose his patients; the patient is free to choose his doctor, he says.

But all is not well. The doctor's younger partner is demoralized. He anxiously points out that statistics show two thirds of people's visits to the doctors are not about proper medical problems. He is overwhelmed with problems for which he does not have an answer. Most people's problems are vague and many primarily of psychological origin. It does not feel like proper doctoring. 'People in an area like this have so many social problems, drinking, wife battering, unemployment, where do you begin?' he says. In his medical training he has done an option in sociology. He talks knowledgeably of the 'cycle of deprivation'. 'People are their own worst enemies', he argues. He does not like giving tranquillizers; 'but what else can you do?'

Our image of the general practitioner has been shaped by folk memories of the country doctor.[2] He is a man who has known the family for generations. They trust him. He comes out at all hours of the day and night. He is wise. Where people's ill health seems linked to bad housing or working conditions, he uses his considerable local standing to pull a few strings. Such doctors may never have existed in large numbers. More likely, there have always been a few of their kind, and some are still alive and well in country or suburban parts of Britain. But they are a minority. In most places people's problems are too overwhelming for the doctor to use his patronage to solve them. Our lives are too complicated, too full of pain for the doctor to bear our troubles or to become intimately involved in them.

The health centre's doctors are bewildered and besieged. They know the problems they see in the surgery have their origins in people's lives. They know that the illness they encounter and the bricks through the window and the slogans on the walls are symptoms of the same condition. But it does not fit with what they learnt at medical school. Symptoms without identifiable pathology, pain without lesion. Their patients do not present with classic symptomatology. Often no clear-cut diseases are readily identifiable. It all seems to be the 'ill-defined conditions' of the giant residual categories in government statistics, which rarely receive discussion in the medical journals. So the sickness is dubbed 'psychogenic'. On one level the doctors are right; our problems may well be psychological in origin; but as we have seen, this does not mean they are necessarily imaginary. As we discussed in Chapter 3, problems manifest themselves in our bodies all the time. It is also true that medicine does not have all the answers, but this does not mean that our health problems are therefore not legitimate. Too often, because we do not fit medicine's model we are left feeling we have illegitimate problems and illegitimate lives.

Unable to cope with our ills, the doctor returns them to us. At medical school he or she has been taught always to offer a diagnosis, always to seem confident in it and never to express doubt. This is the manner in which the doctor now returns his verdict on our troubles. We have only ourselves to blame.

No win blues

The doctor may be demoralized, but we bear the brunt. We come into the surgery with problems that as often as not are intimately linked with the conditions of our lives, our housing, our work, our relationships. In the encounter we find no time to discuss their causes. But, more than that, we can find them dismissed. Elderly people complain of being told 'It's just your age.' Women tire of being made to feel pathologically anxious when they bring their worries to the surgery. We feel ourselves judged. We are eating the wrong things, smoking too much, not fitting in with sexual norms. And we feel undermined. Whatever we try to do about our own health, we never seem to get it right.

What we don't like about seeing the doctor is not just that he or she has little time for us. So often we end up feeling in the wrong. We are either feckless or neurotic. We make too many calls on the health service or too few.

If we fail to take our children for check-ups, we are bad parents. If we are anxious about a fever and call the doctor in the night, we are bad patients. If we fail to go for a cervical smear, we are acting in our own worst interests. If, having been made anxious by the literature in the surgery, we ask for a cervical smear less than five years before the last one, we are making unnecessary demands. If we don't check our breasts for lumps, we are not taking an interest in ourselves. If we report something funny about the rest of our bodies, we come away from the surgery convinced of our mental instability. If we don't go to the family planning clinic, we are feckless. If we do go to the clinic because we want to change the pill for something else, we have been reading too many women's magazines. If we do not take an interest in our health, we are irresponsible. If we do take an interest in our health and go to see the doctor, we are over-demanding.

Our experience in the surgery is reinforced by government agencies and the Department of Health. Health education leaflets urge us to take an interest in our own health. A poster featuring a cartoon of an evidently stupid and irresponsible woman threatens the dire consequences of not going to the antenatal clinic. On the one hand we are encouraged to make demands of the health service; on the other we are told we must not make too many. Posters in the surgery make us feel guilty for calling out the doctor and urge us not to demand too many medicines.

We particularly can't win when it comes to taking the medicine. Doctors complain that patients will not leave the surgery without a prescription, failing to mention the equally large number who do not like taking tablets. Doctors also complain when we fail to take what they prescribe. They call it 'problems of patient compliance' and it has even become a subject for learned articles and academic books.[3] Although they want you to take the drugs, you often don't get instructions on how to take them, and there is not much encouragement to report side effects. Tales of sickness, headaches, dizziness or changes in mood or energy levels often get short shrift. Somehow it seems ungracious to admit what are after all non-life-threatening problems.

The GP is backed up in the belief that patients demand too many pills by the Department of Health, which recently spent thousands on its 'Be prepared to come away empty-handed' campaign. Posters were dispatched to every surgery reinforcing the myth that the NHS's giant drug bill is our fault for demanding too many pills. Nowhere in any of this was any mention of the £50 million or more which could be saved by generic prescribing, which would enable cheaper drugs to be substituted for more expensive ones with the same chemical constituents,[4] or of the £60 million a year paid by the NHS to the drug companies, which is then spent on advertising and promotion.[5]

In the last few years we have heard a lot about people taking more responsibility for their own health. Yet taking responsibility means learning about our bodies, not being passive, asking questions, and making decisions ourselves. We hear over and over again how some people will not take this responsibility. Yet how often do we leave the surgery with half a dozen unanswered questions in our heads? It is not just that the doctor's time is short. There is something about asking questions which does not quite meet with approval. We do not want to fall into the category of the 'difficult' patient. It feels dangerous to encroach upon clearly defined roles. As doctors make clear, there is nothing worse than the patient with a little knowledge. In medical school, doctors learn 'Beware the *Guardian* reader'. But worse than the *Guardian* reader is the working-class person who uses medical terminology or questions the treatment.

We also do not like being cut short when we are telling our tales. Of all the things people say about doctors, 'He starts writing on his pad before you sit down' is surely the most frequent. Too often the doctor has little time for our accounts of our symptoms. We find ourselves cut off a few seconds into our carefully rehearsed account of what the matter is. And if we venture into our pet theories about what it might be or why it came, we are unlikely to get any encouragement. Even with problems like dermatitis from workplace chemicals or industrial asthma, doctors fail to make the connections, because they do not ask the right questions. By not listening the doctor undermines our own insights. These may be wrong or partial, but dialogue with the doctor should deepen our understanding of what is the matter by combining our knowledge of our symptoms and our own lives with his or her general experience and medical knowledge. But this rarely happens. More often we lose confidence in our own perceptions and ability to tackle our problems.

Judging and blaming

Feeling in the wrong, being cut off before we begin, unhappy with drugs, and not getting our questions answered, these are our everyday grumbles. But sometimes the encounter is more painful. We find ourselves judged. Our problems are dismissed and we are left feeling they are the result of our own inadequacies.

In our encounters with general practitioners we are alone. There is no one to hear or judge the doctor's comments. Because we are ill we often feel especially vulnerable. And because it has to do with intimate aspects of our lives we feel exposed. If we take issue, we risk losing our access to treatment. The right to change your doctor is in many instances theoretical. No one wants a difficult patient, and the last thing you feel like doing if you are ill is changing your doctor. For all these reasons, seeing the doctor can be particularly distressing.

What goes on in the surgery is not separate from the outside world. To their consultations with us, doctors bring the values and assumptions of their personal histories and class position. The vast majority of doctors are recruited from families with more money, confidence and power than the majority of people. And doctors who do not share this background often nevertheless find themselves taking on board the ways of seeing and thinking about people in the rest of society which are dominant in hospitals and medical schools. Too often, for women and black doctors in particular, survival means taking on white male values.

The way that many doctors see black people is a stark illustration of medical judging and blaming. A man describes his wife's experience:

In January my wife went to the doctor with a pain in her shoulder. He told her not to worry about it and it would go away. But the pain continued. It was so bad she could not sleep at nights. She went back to the doctor but he sent her away again. Over the next few months the pain got worse and worse. She went back to the doctor three or four times, but he said it was just psychological. In May he finally sent her to hospital, but the hospital doctor said there was nothing wrong. I protested that he should do more tests. Instead they told me that my wife was neurotic and that we had a bad marriage. Finally I was so worried about her the only thing I could think of was to take her straight back to India to see a specialist. She was taken straight off the plane to the hospital, where they diagnosed spinal TB.

It is an extreme case. But it illustrates the power of medical stereotypes.[6] This woman was subject to some of the most common forms of racism in medicine: her pain was not taken seriously; she was seen as neurotic; her family life was blamed for her problems; and a serious illness which is relatively common among recent immigrants, known to be linked to poverty and overcrowding, was overlooked. Instead the woman and her husband were made to feel they were at fault.

It is common to hear the view in the NHS that black people have lower pain thresholds and often moan unnecessarily. The problem is so deep and so widespread that black people with sickle-cell disease often find that the severe pain of a sickle-cell crisis, requiring hospital admission, is not taken seriously. In maternity departments criticisms of black family life are common. Doctors and nurses are critical of the closer relationship with sisters and mothers and the different kind of relationship with husbands which are particularly found in Asian families. Requests to have sisters present at birth, for instance, are not welcomed, because they are seen as disruptive of the bonding between husband and wife.

Real health problems rooted in the social conditions which many black people face and the daily racism they encounter are ignored. In the surgery there is no discussion of the effects of working in sweet-shop factories like the one described by Shan, or of living in damp or overcrowded housing. Most of all the stress of living in constant fear of racist attacks in the streets, estates and the home is ignored. Instead black people find their culture is judged to be at fault. After Shan had collapsed at work she was told sharply by the hospital doctor to stop eating 'yellow stuff' and drinking Coca Cola. Her ill health was blamed on a racist caricature of Asian life-style. Meanwhile the role of the solder in making her ill was not discussed.

In the surgery or consulting room doctors express their personal views. Their ways of seeing things do vary, and they do not all share the common perceptions and prejudices we have described. But these values and attitudes are widespread, partly because they reflect general views held by most people with similar family backgrounds, and partly because they receive extensive support from medical folklore and academic, medical and government institutions.

Commonly held prejudices about black pain thresholds often

assume the status of scientific fact. Amrit Wilson, a journalist, describes how one group of GP's told her with complete scientific detachment: 'The pain threshold for Asians is half that of Caucasians – they complain twice as much for half the reason – they come with minor symptoms.' It is also widely believed that black people cause disease to themselves and other people. In an interview with Amrit Wilson the Department of Health's most senior adviser on ethnic minorities showed no compunction in making the statement: 'Deafness among Asian and African children is probably associated with factors such as lack of hygiene, spitting etc.'[7]

The British Medical Association, Britain's most powerful organization representing doctors, has also played a leading role in spreading the idea that black people cause disease. There is no epidemiological evidence to support the view that if people come into a new country in poor health this will put the general population at risk.[8] Indeed research evidence suggests that, far from bringing TB into the country, people from the Indian subcontinent usually develop it *after* they arrive, because of the living standards they encounter in Britain.[9] Nevertheless between 1956 and 1967 the BMA passed no fewer than twenty-one resolutions demanding the medical screening of immigrants and the exclusion of the unfit.[10]

The attitudes that black people find disturbing are not unique. Medicine has many other stereotypes: the neurotic woman who complains of minor symptoms without a physical cause is another; the Scotsman or Irishman who drinks himself to death is a third. This one has even been rendered respectable by the health educators. The Scottish Health Education Group recently ran a series of advertisements featuring the 'dying Scot', another cartoon stereotype, this time of a working-class man killing himself by drinking and smoking.

We find our sexuality judged too. As a result of the BMA's campaign, people of 'abnormal sexuality' are now also excluded by the immigration rules.[11] It can be very distressing when the doctor makes it clear that our lives do not fit with his or her expectations. A lonely woman, with neither husband nor lover, goes to see the GP about a non-specific pelvic pain. He asks her about her sex life, and tells her cheerfully that this kind of pain is frequently the lot of women without boyfriends. 'They seem to get all seized up inside,' he says. A woman whose husband has left her and her child now has a new boyfriend. At the special clinic she is known by a number and called to see the doctor over a Tannoy. Lying on the couch with her feet in stirrups she feels frightened, powerless and guilty. The pregnant sixteen-year-old is frightened of an injection. 'Of course it will hurt', she is told. 'You should have thought of that before you got into trouble.' The speculum is cold. The gynaecologist remarks 'What's the matter, you are used to things inside you, aren't you?' Having no partner, changing partners, getting pregnant, not getting pregnant, sleeping with people of the same sex, sleeping with people outside marriage – almost any departure from the assumed norm is too often met unsympathetically.

Older people also complain that stereotypes affect the treatment they receive and the attitudes they encounter. Too many problems are seen by doctors as a natural part of ageing. Conditions which in younger people would be taken seriously – like hearing loss – are often not referred for treatment. Aches and pains, distress and worry are dismissed as 'just your age', and pensioners argue that doctors are too ready to see their problems as 'natural' and 'inevitable'.

Victim blaming

In the health service the Victorian term 'feckless' can still be heard. Doctors have always criticized their patients who do not share their social world: 'That woman's problem isn't poverty. She should stand up to her husband. He has always got plenty of beer money, drinks six pints a night.' But over the last few years victim blaming has enjoyed a new respectability. As doctors have increasingly realized that they have limited answers to cancer, heart disease and other chronic health problems, they have neatly shifted the responsibility back to the patient. The problem is our 'health behaviour', smoking, eating and drinking too much and not taking much exercise. We are rarely offered a sympathetic discussion of why it is so difficult to give up smoking or change our eating or drinking habits. It's not just the pressures of advertisers that go unacknowledged; so do the stresses and strains which create the need to eat, drink and smoke. Nor does it occur to most doctors there is no incentive to change your life-style if you've nothing to look forward to, no hope for the future.

Medical institutions and government booklets reinforce the view that we are endangering our own health, while carefully overlooking the many factors which are beyond our individual control. Government leaflets, posters, booklets and even TV programmes proclaim the message. Sometimes what we learn is sympathetic. The Channel Four programme *Well Being*, made in conjunction with the Royal College of General Practitioners, spelt out the difficulties as well as the 'oughts' about changing eating habits and overcoming addictions. But too often what we are told is at best patronizing and at worst absurd. The Health Education Council issues little booklets to pensioners at risk of hypothermia because they can't afford the heating, advising them to 'Ask visitors if it seems cold to them in your house and take their advice'[12] – as if pensioners sit in the cold through ignorance of the value to health of keeping warm.

The government funds and guides priorities in health education. But in addition it makes its own contribution to the guilt tripping and victim blaming. A series of booklets on prevention urge us to change our health behaviour. The one on healthy eating[13] does not mention the role of the food companies in the manufacture of profitable junk food or the emotional stresses that lead to compulsive eating. The pamphlet on preventing heart disease[14] gives a detailed description of the 'risk factors' in heart disease, but fails to mention that the risk is greater for working-class people, or that the jobs we do also affect the risk. The booklet on healthy babies[15] again urges early attendance at the antenatal clinic. It does not ask why some women stay away, or why others might find it impossible to get time off work.

Keeping us down

Coming face to face with prejudices based on age, race, gender and sexuality and with other judgemental attitudes is hurtful and distressing. But the problem extends beyond the encounter itself, or the treatment we receive. Doctors can also help or hinder us in our relations with employers, landlords and official bodies.

Refusal to provide sick notes is one major area of contention. The woman is distraught. She has been off work for ten days with flu and still feels weak and giddy. She works in a big food-canning factory. The doctor has refused to give her a certificate and says she must go back to work. She cannot afford to lose a day's pay, especially as it also means losing her bonus. But she is afraid to go back to work, because she fears she will fall into the machine.

Doctors can also play a crucial role in legitimizing or under-mining demand for better housing. In the past doctors have been helpful in pressing for rehousing, but increasingly they are being pressured by District Medical Officers, who liaise with councils to assess medical priority for rehousing. The DMOs are insisting that doctors restrict their support for patients in housing need, as a way of preventing demand becoming uncontrollable. 'You can't put a quart into a pint pot', they say.[16] Many DMOs are now restricting the categories of illness seen as legitimate grounds for rehousing. In most areas 'mental instability' no longer counts, unless corroborated by a consultant psychiatrist, because the demand for rehousing on these grounds has become so high.

The factory doctor is an old labour movement bogey. He takes the side of management and overlooks hazards which cost money to remedy. Factory doctors are mainly GPs who take on the work to supplement their income. In a recent series in *General Practitioner* magazine they talk about their work. A doctor for a Ford foundry is quoted as saying 'You have to be realistic in this job. The plant is a noisy, smelly place to work and the only way you could give workers total protection would be to close it down.' He admits that the introduction of a new process combined greater efficiency with the use of a 'rather nasty toxic substance', but says 'Fords is a commercial company and we have to accept that the new process is an excellent one that works well and is efficient, although the hazards of using it are quite high.'[17] Another doctor for a chemical company says he sees one aspect of his job as translating 'medicalese'. 'It is useful for both workers and management to know for instance that "carcinogenic" means that the substance may bring forward the onset of cancer rather than cause it.'

Both Les Bennett and Andrew Tree comment on the role of senior doctors in legitimizing the *status quo* and criticize their failure to support their struggles for better health. Andrew said 'Every time the company has got in specialist doctors the purpose has been to reassure us.' In his efforts to clean up the plant, doctors were a hindrance rather than a help. Les was also unable to get support from the medical profession, either to assist in individual cases or in highlighting housing need:

Doctors could be more forthcoming when they write their letters substantiating the tenants' claim for rehousing. Some doctors are compassionate and not afraid to say these conditions should not exist. But where you get one like that, there are a dozen that will not. I did contact the Medical Officer of Health and ask for his support in one or two cases. But I found it was a question of the old routine of passing the buck: 'I feel it is not my place to intervene.' Three years ago I also contacted him about how far the bad conditions are likely to resurrect TB and the possible flare-up of the allied complaints of asthma, bronchitis and arthritis. We asked him to support us, to give a medical opinion. But no go. He did not want to put his head on the block.

In hospital

At the hospital, as outpatients, and even more so as in-patients, our relationships with doctors change. Some of the vague complaints which the general practitioner sees much of the time have been screened out and people are more likely to be 'really' ill. Our illness fits the medical model. So, especially when life itself is at stake, there is less victim blaming, more compassion. We are iller, more vulnerable, more dependent, and also more passive, pleased by smaller things and far more conscious of life and death, far more grateful about what is done for us.

But the coin has another side. One reason why we feel less at fault is that the hospital doctor focuses on our diseases rather than on us as people inhabiting a social world. In hospital the people we are gets left behind. We are known by the names of our diseased organs – 'the query ectopic in the third bed down'.

All of which makes the problem of intervening in our own treatment, understanding what is happening to our bodies, asking questions and asserting our right to make choices about our treatment even more difficult in hospital than it is in the GP's surgery. The class difference between ourselves and the hospital doctor often seems even greater, and he or she appears even more pressed for time than the GP. And when our health problems are serious, the anxiety about what the answer to our questions is going to be is even more profound. The atmosphere in the hospital does not encourage questioning. In many hospitals patients are still forbidden to read their own charts hanging at the bottom of the bed. So to seek information we have to take hold of our fear in both hands. If the doctors are busy and their manner is distant, this is even more difficult.

Many doctors are themselves confused about the patient's right to information. In some ways medical training – and nurse training too – can be seen as an initiation into ways of repressing distress at patients' suffering. During training there is little discussion about how to come to terms with the pain and sadness you encounter. Medical – and nursing – students shed their tears in the lavatory. So when it comes to deciding what to tell patients about their illnesses, doctors also have their own problem to face of how to handle the upset which imparting their knowledge can bring.

Particularly if the ill person is dying there are no easy answers. It is hard to translate an abstract right to information into practice, sensitively interpreting what the ill person wants to know. Some people believe that the unspoken and private fear you might be dying is worse than the shared knowledge that you are. At present, however, barriers of fear are erected between the doctor, the ill person and the relatives. In some hospitals patients with cancer are still told they have 'ulcers' or 'bladder warts'. Elsewhere uncertainty about what to tell the patient puts the onus on the ill person in a cruel way. A friend has cancer. When she was told by the doctor she had a tumour she asked 'Benign or malignant?' When he said he could not tell her, it was left to her to say 'Then I must assume it is malignant.'

Silence

When we look at what is going on in our relationships with doctors, at what it is we don't like, there is a pattern to it. The most important thing about the pattern is the silence. From the level of government policy to doctors' everyday practice in the surgery, there is silence about what is making us ill. It is as if the world described by Shan and Vera and the rest did not exist. At best illness comes from nowhere, striking at random. At worst it is the consequence of our own inadequacies.

The problem with the health service goes beyond the mixed-up priorities of clinical dominance we identified in the last chapter. Our health care system ignores our social world, not just by failing to recognize our non-clinical health care needs but by reinforcing an enormous gulf between our illness and the world which gives rise to it. So often our experience – of evictions, redundancies, productivity deals, of hazardous work or domestic or racist violence, of all the forces which are destructive of our health – seems to go unacknowledged. It is blanked out. It is not mentioned in the surgery or in the hospital. It rarely forms part of the snippets on health we receive from television and in the newspapers. It is not there in health education leaflets, and there is no sign of it in government publications.

Medical practice compounds the silence by turning it in upon ourselves. It is as if medicine has created a powerful force field bending our perceptions of health and illness away from the forces which destroy our health and back on to us as individuals. We have seen some of the components of this force field: where the origins of our ill health are not shrouded in silence, they are presented to us as illegitimate; medicine pays attention to those aspects of our ill health which it puts down to our personal failures; it is difficult to ask questions or to begin to take control of our own bodies; the social values which we identify as destructive of health, like racism and sexism, are frequently reinforced by doctors; and doctors' class perspectives so often reinforce rather than challenge the anti-health policies and practices of other agencies, like housing departments and employers.

In the first part of this book we explored the way in which the struggles of everyday life – personal struggles with social security officials, housing departments and the like, and collective struggles at work and in the neighbourhood – are so often about health. Every day we confront the health-destructive forces in our lives. Too often in these struggles the doctor is not on our side, reinforcing rather than challenging dominant attitudes which damage our health. In our encounters with medicine the social relations which are the preconditions of our continued exploitation and oppression are daily reproduced. Medicine ignores the social origins of our ill health and undermines our everyday struggle for survival and a better life. It oils the wheels which prevent us from saying 'No, enough!'[18]

Wise men used to take care to consult doctors qualified before 1860, who were usually contemptuous of or indifferent to the germ theory and bacteriological therapeutics; but we are left in the hands of the generations which, having heard of microbes much as St Thomas Aquinas heard of angels, suddenly concluded that the whole art of healing could be summed up in the formula: Find the microbe and kill it.

George Bernard Shaw[1]

We are angry with medicine because we do not like the way many doctors treat us. We do not like the attitudes and values we so often encounter. As we have seen, they are a way of maintaining silence on what is making us ill. But the role of medicine in reproducing the social relations which make us sick is not only to do with the *manner* in which doctors respond to our needs. The process by which the connection between our lives and our health is obscured is not only to do with its practitioners' behaviour towards us. It is also a matter of medicine's framework of thinking, the way it looks at health and illness and its concepts of disease and pathology. The problem is not only the way doctors relate to their patients, but the very medical science through which they are relating.

We often think of science as outside of and separate from politics. It has a status, a solidity, a dignity which leads us to see it as value-free. Medical science is no exception. Yet in practice – as with most science – it becomes impossible to separate an inner core of 'pure' medical knowledge from an outer shell of manners and values. We cannot avoid looking critically at basic ideas in medicine: the concept of diagnosis, medicine's understanding of the relationships between the head and the body and of the disease process. Medicine's conceptual structure does correspond to biological phenomena, but the question is whether it is the only way of looking at things. Is medicine's view of health and illness, the structure of ideas in which all its activities take place, helping or hindering our understanding of what ails us or of possibilities for healing?

Looking inside

We learn from childhood that the place to look for explanations of our suffering is inside our bodies. We are taught that the answers lie in biology, in working out what is going wrong and putting it right. Images of devoted men and women toiling night and day in laboratories come to mind. We think of Louis Pasteur and Alexander Fleming. We know as second nature what medicine must do in its battle against disease. First it must locate the biological agency of the illness. Then it can act against the disorder. We remember the discovery of penicillin and the other antibiotics. First came the recognition that disease is carried by bacteria. Then a drug to combat those bacteria was developed. This adversarial view of treatment conceives of healing as a pitched battle between doctor and disease.[2]

The 'battle-against-disease' model of the way illness is dealt with is so deeply ingrained in our culture that it seems a heresy to question it. But, as we have seen, there are other ways of thinking about the 'causes' of illness. Medicine could put more emphasis on biography rather than biology, looking for causes at the level of feelings, experiences and social forces. Medicine's present explanations of illness are primarily at the level of cell chemistry and microbiology. Although medicine is now beginning to acknowledge multi-causal influences on health, for instance in the aetiology of heart disease, the explanations it still finds most satisfying are ones on the level of cells and molecules; they fit the model of how it should be.

The problem, however, is that medicine never seems to come

up with the final 'cause' of a condition. And even if it reaches the point where it discovers what gene, what hormone, what enzyme is finally at fault, this often does not lead to more effective treatment. There seems so often to be an infinite regression, with few final answers, which is why there are so few final cures (and so many side effects). Medicine's pursuit of single causes is bolstered by the organization of medical practice, with its specialisms in different organ systems – cardiology, neurology and the rest – which act as a barrier to seeing whole bodies and whole people. More and more, however, this view of illness as localized in particular organ systems, rather than having effects throughout the body, is not making sense. Take rheumatoid arthritis. It can affect the skin, the eyes, the kidneys, heart, lungs and blood system, and it has also been suggested that it is linked with emotional factors. While at a theoretical level there is a recognition of the complexity of many diseases, the practice of medicine is still fragmented.

Medicine prefers uni-causal models of explanations, but recent developments in Western medicine make the dream of finding final, single explanations ever more remote. Vaisrub, in an article called 'Groping for Causation' in the *Journal of the American Medical Association*,[3] puts it this way:

New cybernetic mechanisms have added further complexities to understanding causality in human physiology. Cause and effect no longer bear a straight linear relationship to each other. Circular mechanisms of positive and negative feedback have taken over in the operational depths of homeostasis. The chain of causation is fast dissolving before our eyes to be replaced by some form of invariable association that does not lend itself readily to a graphic, mathematical or any other representation.

Larry Dossey, an American physician, in his book *Space, Time and Medicine*,[4] which draws on Vaisrub, argues that it is now impossible to think of any disease as having a single cause:

Even in the infectious diseases, which we once believed to be the result of a straightforward balance between the aggressiveness of the micro-organism and the defence capabilities of the host, we have entered Vaisrub's 'operational depths of homeostasis'. We do not know with certainty, for example, why some persons when challenged with strepto-coccal infection contract rheumatic fever, while others may develop 'strep throat', or why some people may become an asymptomatic carrier of the bacterium, or why others repel the organism completely.

The reasons, we supposed, were at least shrouded in the workings of the cells of our bodies. We presumed that we could eventually decipher all the factors involved – and even if we did not yet know *how* to look for them, at least we knew *where* to look: in the body itself, or in the bacterium. But, alas, even that presumption has proved illusory, for we have discovered that we do not know precisely what we meant by 'body'. For in investigating our resistance to infection, we know that the map of the body must include the mind.

For a more appropriate view of the nature and origins of illness it may be necessary to go back to Eastern conceptions, which see illness as an imbalance in the mind-body system, a conception reminiscent of Vaisrub's 'circular mechanism of positive and negative feedback'. This notion of whole bodies whose wellbeing is disrupted is there in common language too, summed up as 'out of sorts'.

We must look to new conceptions of causality, not because it is philosophically pleasing, but because the old ones are not delivering the goods. The discovery of the physiological cor-relates and proximate causes of disease is not providing abundant cures. Occasionally the model works – so we have cures for Hodgkin's disease or pernicious anaemia. But given the enormous effort presently being put into this kind of research, there have been relatively few real breakthroughs. The pharmaceutical companies, who carry out more than half the medical research in Britain, have a particular vested interest in devising specific biochemical means to attack illness. There are super-profits to be made. But in four decades there has not been another success story of the dimensions of the discovery of antibiotics. Viruses have been tracked down, but there has been no biochemical agent found which will tackle them. More and more is being learned about the biochemistry of cancer, down to the genetic structure of the cancer cell, but despite regular reports in the press of new breakthroughs, bringing a cancer cure ever nearer, little practical application has been found for what has been learned.

Although in other fields, from sociology to psychology, and from systems theory to atomic physics, it is acknowledged that the whole is greater than the parts, this view still has only a limited place in medicine, where the body continues to be seen as a mass of biochemical processes. Medicine is still trying to understand health and illness by summing the parts, attempting to understand the whole by trying to know more and more about all the little bits. Technological innovations are all about looking closer to see deeper. The electron microscope becomes a metaphor for the whole process. Yet with all the resources in the world there is no reason to believe the project will succeed. More knowledge will be generated, but whether this knowledge can be applied to healing is another question.

The model for medical research is also the model for understanding specific illnesses in specific people. We have become so used to clinical investigations as the primary route to understanding what is the matter that it never occurs to us to question whether the doctor is looking in the right place. The nuclear magnetic resonance scanner for investigating soft tissue in the body is the most recent of a whole series of diagnostic tools, going back to the stethoscope, devised to probe ever deeper.[5] The scanner may be very much more sophisticated than the stethoscope, but the project for which it has been devised is essentially the same: to look *inside* for explanations.[6] Obviously in many instances this is one appropriate course of action. But in many others it may be of equal therapeutic relevance to look outside, in addition to or instead of, internal diagnostic measures.

In the poem, written over forty years ago, which opens this book, the poet Bertolt Brecht makes the same point: 'Our rags are torn off us', he says, 'And you listen all over our naked body.

As to the cause of our illness One glance at our rags would Tell
you more.'

Discrete diseases

Just as we have been taught to see the causes of illness primarily
in terms of biology, we have been taught to see illness in a very
particular way. Diseases are discrete entities which invade our
bodies. Illness becomes a thing inhabiting us but separate from
us. We 'get it', 'catch it', 'get rid of it', 'shake it off'. It is
discontinuous from our normal life. In some ways this separation
is helpful. Knowing we have a disease somehow takes away our
responsibility for it. But it also helps to build the myth that illness
comes from nowhere. Seeing disease as a thing rather than a
process – a noun rather than an adjective or even a verb – as
discrete from, rather than continuous with, our daily existence
obscures from us the possibility of recognizing its origins in our
conditions of life.

Shan speaks of the way seeing illness as disease obscured from
her colleagues the origins of their ill health in their work:

> But people would say as an excuse 'I've got flu.' Now if you explain
> flu to somebody, they would not understand what flu you were talking
> about. I think it was the majority view that because you have got cold
> running down your nose you say 'I've got flu.' But it could be because
> they were run down, or from the compressed air ... or the soldering
> fumes.

Shan sees illness as a process rather than a thing: 'cold running
down your nose'. She is critical of the women she worked with
because they have been mystified into seeing it as an entity, 'flu',
disconnected from their lives. In the interviews there are other
forms of expression which reflect a more dynamic conception of
the relation between our lives and our illness than the classical
disease model. Shan says that factory conditions 'can bring your
sinus down'; Vera talks of being 'weakened into bronchitis'.

Diagnosis

One of the ways we are educated into seeing illness as discrete diseases is through the naming system medicine has developed. It is clearly useful to have some system for classifying symptoms and causes, but medicine attaches a special significance to the names it gives diseases. They are more than names, they are *diagnoses*. To make a diagnosis is to imply a knowledge of the cause, and thus the cure. The dictionary defines disease as a disorder with recognizable signs and symptoms and *with a specific cause*.[7]

Naming becomes an almost magical act of optimism. If we are given a name for a collection of symptoms which tend to go together, this implies we will soon be *en route* to cure. How often people say 'It will be all right once they find out what it is.' Yet how often does naming a condition result in cure? As we have already pointed out, to know the biological cause is rarely to be able to offer a cure. And how many so-called 'diseases' are no more than names for a collection of symptoms without known cause or cure? How many times have we emerged from the surgery having been told we have 'non-specific urethritis' or 'irritable bowel syndrome'? The doctor may have impressed us with his or her diagnosis, but all we have been told is that we have symptoms with no known cause. After two years of going to the hospital about her three-year-old's chronic severe diarrhoea, Vera was told she had toddler's diarrhoea: 'I said to them "So you don't actually know what it is?" They said "No, we don't actually know what it is."'

Having an illness named can be very comforting. It may be a useful, if slightly pompous, way of telling someone they have not got a major killer disease. Being given a diagnosis often comes as a relief. But there is a kind of way in which we are being conned. A diagnosis can be a false reassurance. Thomas McKeown is sceptical about doctors' obsession with diagnosis:

There seems to be an inverse relation between the interest of a disease to the doctor and the usefulness of its treatment to the patient. Neurology, for example, was highly regarded and attracted some of the best minds because of the fascination of its diagnostic problems, but the precision of diagnosis, which was the focus of medical interest, made not the slightest difference to the outcome.[8]

There is a further problem with medicine's diagnostic categories. In teaching us to see illnesses as different from one another it makes us lose sight of their similarities. If I have persistent headaches while someone else I work with gets ulcers, we tend not to think of the possibility that our different conditions may have a common cause. Some epidemiologists have suggested that in trying to understand the causes of illness it is more important to look at the general state of health of groups of people than to focus exclusively on particular conditions. Diagnostic categories can fragment our collective experience.

Body and mind

The emphasis on biological causality and the concept of disease as a thing are reinforced by the separation of the head and the body which is at the heart of medicine. We learn that our minds – our psychology – can be affected by the social world, but that our bodies are only affected by the physical world. We are taught that the way the outside world impinges on the body is through harmful agents – germs, viruses, alcohol, food, carcinogens and so on. Normally people's life experience is not assumed to affect their bodies unless this gives rise to contact with harmful agents. Where there is an illness there must be some kind of pathogen.

More recently the notion that illness can be linked with life events, such as the death of a spouse, has been recognized but not yet addressed in therapy. Where it is acknowledged that people's feelings, thoughts, emotions or experience affect their health, for instance in ulcers or asthma, this is seen as unusual. These illnesses are given a special category, *psychosomatic*. Some doctors have shown great interest in them, but for the majority they are seen at best as a curiosity, an anomaly, or at worst as not real illness. The term psychosomatic has passed into common language as a word for illness *which does not really exist*. When we go to the doctor with symptoms which have no physical cause we are often told our problems are 'just psychological'. We come away with the feeling they are illegitimate. The number of illnesses for which doctors have posited a psychological dimension must run into hundreds: high blood pressure, asthma, ulcers, eczema and back pain are just a few common ones. Every other decade or so there is a surge of interest in the psychological dimensions of illness. In the 1930s, for instance, under the influence of psychoanalysis there was a vogue for psychosomatic explanations, and more recently considerable attention has been paid to the role of stress in heart disease. But the head/body separation has been so powerful that all these exceptions to the rule have not been sufficient to restructure medicine's way of thinking.

Battle of ideas

In some ways it seems outrageous for lay people to question medical concepts. How can we be sure we even know what they are if we have not been to medical school? The answer is that as lay people we know about health and illness what medicine wants to teach us about it. In the surgery, in school, from television and the newspapers, we pick up 'common-sense' ideas. These do not come out of the blue. They are shaped by medicine. Our understanding comes out of our experience of its practice and what we are told of its achievements. We learn almost instinctively, as part of our culture, that illness is caused by germs; that sickness is either 'in your head' or 'real'; that the way to cure illness is to identify a disease, give it a name, understand its pathology and attack what is causing it. It is what medicine itself has taught us that we question.

There is a philosophical argument to be had, but this does not mean it is an obscure one. The battle is not a closed-door academic affair. It is going on every day out in the world in our encounters with medicine. For the view of health and illness medicine constructs through its practice is not being offered to fifty million blank consciousnesses. Medicine is battling against another view of health and illness also embodied in our culture. We are 'worried sick'; we know we are 'run down'; we need to get things 'out of our system'; we feel sure someone's illness was caused by his wife's death and so on. This other view is the perspective within which Baden, Vera, Ruth and most of the others see their lives and their health. They are acutely aware of the inter-relatedness of our health and the feelings our life circumstances give rise to. Everyday medical practice asserts the dominant perspective against the opposition of this other view.

People's understanding of health and illness is shaped both by their experience and by their encounters with medicine. Health workers who are critical of medicine's framework report that people talk about their illnesses in two different ways. They start off using medicine's terminology: 'It's to do with my thrombosis'; 'My angina's playing me up.' But with encouragement people go on to confide tentatively in terms of the second approach – 'My job is killing me'; 'That flat is wearing me out' – but not expecting this kind of view to be validated by a health professional. Most people do not have a fully coherent, worked-out perspective, but they are often carrying around two separate ways of looking at illness in their heads at once. It would be wrong and romantic to imply that working-class people have a natural understanding of all the issues. Nevertheless, medical practice is in daily struggle with another set of assumptions which are to do with people's real, felt class experience.

Blinding light

The concepts of pathology, disease and diagnosis and of organic and psychosomatic illness are at the centre of medicine. But they extend far beyond the world of white coats and laboratories, deep into our everyday lives. The way medicine has taught us to think about health and illness has become deeply embedded in our culture. It is so familiar we all use its way of looking at things without thinking twice about it: 'I've got hypertension' or 'It's just psychological'. Medical talk is so natural it is hard to see it as specific to our culture, our period in history and our present form of social organization.

Medicine's explanatory concepts are so deeply embedded in us that we sometimes find ourselves without words to express any other way of looking at things, the way we tried to describe in Part One of this book. We have only the words 'physical' and 'psychological', no term to describe the impact of feelings and emotions on the body. We have only the colloquial 'weak at the knees', 'lump in my throat', 'knot in my stomach', 'butterflies in my tummy', or the Eastern terminology of energy flows, chis and chakras to describe the way particular feelings affect us.[9] We have also no satisfactory term for the non-biological realm of causality. We call it the social world. But it is more. It is emotional, political, economic. We have only the slightly mystical and old-fashioned word 'spirit' to describe the realm of experience which has to do with neither heads nor bodies, the realm of meaning and meaninglessness, of loneliness and connection, of boredom and fulfilment, which bears on our health.

The issue is not one of priorities. The argument here is not that, by concentrating on microbiology, for instance, resources are being limited for epidemiology. It is that internalizing medicine's concepts of health and illness makes it more difficult to see the connection between our health and our lives. Medicine offers a partial view of the world. No one can deny that germs are present in infection or that people with high blood cholesterol have more heart attacks. The problem is that this framework blinds medicine, and more importantly the rest of us, to other ways of seeing. The everyday practice of medicine involves continually constructing and reconstructing a view of illness which denies both its social nature and our own capacity to begin to take control of our own health. Thus the *status quo* is reproduced.

9 Crisis and Restructuring

The 'Central Hospital' in the Introduction to this book is a fictional name for a real hospital. In the four months between writing the Introduction and this chapter it has become clear that the Central Hospital may be closed. It is the victim of a recent policy initiative by the Department of Health. Every Regional Health Authority was asked to review the efficiency of its hospitals. The minister received reports on throughput, bed occupancy rates, costs per patient-day and other indicators of good management. Despite the stresses and strains on the people who work in and use this high-productivity hospital, the Central Hospital has been judged still not productive enough. All new building programmes for the hospital have been stopped and, while denying closure rumours vehemently, the Regional Health Authority has refused to give any assurances about the hospital's future.

As in many other parts of the country, this latest threatened closure is the most recent in a series of increasingly desperate moves to balance the books by reducing staff and services. Since 1976 the Central Hospital's district has lost over a quarter of its 1,200 beds. Two other hospitals have been closed and turned over to geriatric care in the productivity drive. For local people the rationalization has meant longer journeys to hospital, longer waits when you get there, longer waiting lists, earlier discharge and more frequent readmission. For people who have to make regular visits as outpatients or visitors, especially if they are unwell, are elderly or have young children, the longer journey, which now involves two or three buses, can be miserable. If the Central Hospital closes, the people who now use it will have to travel even further afield, to other hospitals under increasing pressure of work. All the difficulties of struggling to get to hospital, surviving once you get there and managing when you are sent home will be magnified.

The new efficiency drive is the latest in a line of government policies in response to what is often called the 'crisis' in the NHS. Whether it can properly be called a crisis is doubtful. The NHS has been impoverished and burdened with decaying hospitals since its inception. Nevertheless since the International Monetary Fund told the then Labour government to curtail public spending in 1976, health authorities have been expected to manage on ever tighter budgets. Spending on staff and running costs has been gradually squeezed and money for maintenance and new developments halved. Along with the cutbacks there has been a spate of new initiatives by Labour and Conservative administrations promising to resolve the NHS's ills. Although the basic problem has been the need for more money, the new policies have uniformly been about getting by on less. The policies touch almost every aspect of NHS work: resource distribution, health service organization, health propaganda, administrative and medical practice. Two things are interesting about them. The first is that each policy embraced in its rhetoric recent criticisms of the NHS. The other is that although facilities within the NHS are steadily declining, nothing to do with its power structure, priorities, ideology or practice has fundamentally changed.

No ball for Cinderella

As the beginning of the squeeze on public spending loomed in the mid-1970s the Labour government, realizing the size of the cake was not going to grow, announced a redistribution of it. The redistribution was to take two forms.[1] First, there was to be an end of the policy of 'to those that have shall be given'. Those parts of the country, like the Trent and East Anglia regions, which had until now received less money because they had fewer services were to get an increased share of new money. Those, particularly the London regions, who had previously been given more money because they had more services were to have their growth restricted. This was R A W P, following the initials of the Resources Allocation Working Party.[2]

Second, recognizing the enormous inequality between the standard of care in general hospitals and those in hospitals for the elderly and the mentally handicapped and psychiatric hospitals, it was agreed that resources should be redistributed to what became known as the 'Cinderella sector'.

Both policies seemed fine in principle. But what the policy-makers did not choose to take account of was that their policies left intact the power structure which had determined the distribution of resources in the first place.

The poorer regions were to get growth money, but as the squeeze on spending deepened, there was no growth. Both Labour and Conservative administations barely succeeded in finding the 1 per cent per year needed to keep up with the growing number of elderly people in the population. The Conservatives invented the device of clawing half of it back in 'efficiency' savings. The effect has been that while the historically under-resourced regions have found themselves with barely the resources to maintain services at their present level, the four London regions have found themselves operating on reduced budgets.

Faced with ever-growing expenditure engendered by innovation in medicine, particularly in the teaching hospitals, and with budgets squeezed to an all-time low, health authorities in the London region set about implementing that part of the Cinderella policy which legitimized reducing the acute sector. The planners observed low throughput in the smaller hospitals, and these became the primary target for closure. In the 'over-resourced' regions one small hospital after another closed, despite bitter resistance. Some, like Hounslow and the Elizabeth

Garrett Anderson, became a *cause célèbre*, but for each of the famous ones there were many struggles which did not make the headlines.[3]

Although some redistribution between regions has been achieved – now people in Trent have 30 per cent less spent on them than people in the North West Thames Region; in 1976 it was 45 per cent[4] – the Cinderella exercise has released few resources for the long-stay sector.[5] Between 1970 and 1980 the proportion of the budget spent on acute hospitals actually went *up*. In 1970–71 acute services received 53 per cent of the budget[6]; in 1980–81 they received 57 per cent. Meanwhile the amount spent on hospitals for the mentally ill and the mentally handicapped *decreased* slightly, from 18 per cent in 1970–71 down to 17 per cent in 1980–81. Furthermore, despite the shift in philosophy from hospital to community care, the community services' share of the budget has gone down from 10.5 per cent in 1968 to 6.2 per cent in 1980.[7] The size of the cake has shrunk, but the interests which have always determined its distribution have not abated.

The result is that while care for the mentally ill, mentally handicapped and elderly has not benefited significantly, everyday health care in the acute sector is also losing out. The smaller hospitals tend to cater for people whose illnesses require more bed rest, nursing and care than sophisticated medicine. High-pressure, high-throughput hospitals are not geared to their needs. As we saw in Chapter 5, in high-productivity hospitals the subordination of care to medical intervention is intensified. At the same time all the difficulties of travel to and from hospital for outpatients, visitors and people who have had accidents are increased when they have to go further afield.

Many of the hospitals which were seen to be particularly inefficient were in inner-city areas. Here people tend to stay in hospital longer, because they are often older, more seriously ill, take longer to recover and are less likely to have homes which are suitable for getting better in. So throughput is low. It rarely seems to occur to planners looking at norms and throughput to ask whether the beds in the small hospitals are empty or full or to think about where all the people presently occupying them will go. Many of the old small general hospitals have now become geriatric hospitals. The pensioners they claim to serve protest that this segregation is far from the special care they would like to see. These new ghettoes differ little from those we described in Chapter 5. And they continue to be under-staffed, because no one wants to work in them.

Until very recently all the closures have been made by health authorities on the assumption that, although the number of beds will be reduced, the same number of patients will be seen, by getting them through hospital faster. As we have seen, such policies have considerable costs to staff and patients. Now, however, a further shift in approach is occurring. Hospital managers are beginning to intimate that the costs of acute care are still too high, even with the maximum 'intensity of use' of hospital beds. Recent forward plans of some health authorities indicate that the next stage is to *reduce* throughput and hospitalization rates, which means admitting fewer people to hospital.

Care(?) in the community

In addition to trying to get short-term patients out of general hospitals quicker, the policy-makers have not been slow to recognize the even greater money-saving possibilities of keeping the long-term sick out of hospital altogether. Shortly after the introduction of the Cinderella policy, there was a small rash of new building on hospital sites throughout the country. 'Rehabilitation', an important but previously neglected aspect of health care, was on every administrator's tongue. The health planners had realized that some of the money saved by closing general hospitals could be spent on getting people out of hospital. The new psychotropic drugs had made psychiatric illness far more manageable, and it was recognized that many mentally ill as well as elderly and mentally handicapped people need not be in hospital if their families looked after them. Suddenly all the criticisms which had been made of long-stay hospitals for many years became respectable in the mid-1970s. Everyone agreed that no one really wanted to be in hospital and that hospitals were dreadful places really. The idea of getting people out was positive. The problem was that making a good job of community care is probably at least as expensive as caring for people in hospital.[8] The only way that community care could work was by not spending enough money on caring for people at home, and exploiting women's unpaid labour as carers.

Many of the developments in rehabilitation which followed the new philosophy have been excellent. Elderly people who would have previously spent the rest of their lives in hospital are taught to walk and look after themselves again. Day centres for the mentally ill offer art, dance and group therapy. Mentally handicapped children who might have been abandoned to institutions are taught to feed themselves and keep themselves clean.

But while some resources have gone into getting or keeping people out of hospital, far fewer have been used on caring for people once sent home. For elderly people living on their own and women caring for dependent relatives, coping at home can be a nightmare. There is rarely help with laundry or transport, or an evening or night sitting service to enable the people caring to get out. The district nurse never quite comes when you expect her and always seems under pressure. There is the day centre, but the journey is long and uncomfortable, and sometimes the ambulance does not turn up because they are short of drivers. The cuts in local authority services, which have generally been even harsher than those in the NHS, have compounded these difficulties. More pressure is continually being put on fewer services. A shortage of home helps, meals on wheels, and money to adapt homes so that they are suitable for ill and disabled people has intensified the problems created by the policy of keeping people out of hospital wherever possible.

For people without relatives able to look after them or who are unable to live on their own, real community care will only be possible when there are purpose-designed homes with paid staff to look after them. To care for people well is expensive, and neither local councils nor health authorities have the money for this side of the community care package. A cottage in the grounds of an old asylum has been designated a training house for mentally handicapped people who will later be moved into 'the community'. It takes four people at a time. Over the past year several groups of people who have lived in the hospital for years have learned in the cottage to shop, cook and get on with each other. But because there is nowhere for them to go, no money for the group homes jointly planned by the local authority and the local council, each group has had to return to the anonymous world of thirty in a ward, cold food and compulsory bedtimes.

Going private

While many parts of the health service come under even greater pressure, the private sector has expanded in a way which is unprecedented since the inception of the NHS. In 1981 fifty new private hospitals were under construction. Subscriptions to private medical insurance companies rose by 15.6 per cent in 1979, 27 per cent in 1980 and by 23 per cent in the first half of 1981. It was a boom period for the private medical companies attracting foreign investors as well as British capital.[9]

With the Conservative government investigating possible schemes for financing the health service through health insurance as soon as it came to office in 1979, some people interpreted these developments as signalling the end of the National Health Service. More recently, however, the government appears to have dropped its interest in establishing an insurance-based service, and the growth in subscription rates to private health insurance companies has also levelled off to around 4–5 per cent each year. BUPA, which insures three of the four million people with private cover, was much less confident by the end of 1982 than it was at the beginning of 1981. In 1981 it made a loss of £1.9 million, mainly due to unexpectedly high claim rates. The *Financial Times* commented: 'The rise in members as the associations widened their net and went further down the social scale, meant a disproportionate increase in claims. This was predictable because the worse off someone is financially the poorer health that person tends to enjoy.'[10] Private health care is profitable only when it is sold to those who do not get sick.

Although there is money to be made out of health care, it is only in limited areas, particularly medium-technology non-urgent operations. The scale of investment required for many modern medical procedures is too high to guarantee adequate returns if private hospitals were themselves to treat all conditions. There is most money to be made while the private sector is in a symbiotic relationship with the health service. At the moment the only way that private companies can offer comprehensive care is by paying for the person to have treatment in NHS hospitals if they are very seriously ill. At the other end of the scale, private health insurance companies are not interested in the vast numbers of ill people who are likely to need long-term care. If you are over sixty-five or chronically ill the cost of private health insurance is prohibitive. Most insurance arrangements have carefully worded clauses limiting the company's liability for long-term care.

The advantages to the government of a switch to an insurance-based system seem on balance to be minimal. The cost of administration is expensive and the number of people for whom the state would still be required to provide safety-net care, including pensioners, the unemployed, single-parent families and people on low incomes, would be considerable. And it is the people who are not able to insure themselves, particularly the elderly, the disabled and the chronically ill, who are most frequently in need of health care. So the possibilities of further reducing the cost of health care through insurance are small. Most recently the government has become more interested in subcontracting NHS work to private firms. This may not save a lot of money, but could lead to even lower wages for health workers and poorer standards of care, as well as undermining trade union organization.

It is always possible that we may be threatened by a change in the financing of the health service, and it is right to be vigilant. What is important about the growth of private medicine for the time being, however, is that it has provided a way out for better-off people who are not prepared to accept the deteriorating standards in the health service. Private health care is a safety valve for all the people who can afford it and would otherwise kick up a fuss about long waits, short staffing and overstretched facilities. When the health service was set up it was to be a comprehensive service for the whole population, and it could justly claim that it realized this ideal, to the extent that very few people in its first decades were sufficiently dissatisfied with it to subscribe to private health insurance. Today the NHS is no longer a service for everybody. It can no longer claim to offer comprehensive care. Despite the spate of policies intended to make a better job of getting by on less, those who can afford to do so have voted with their feet. Sadly we must recognize that the health service has become a second-class service for those – the majority – who cannot afford otherwise.

Looking after ourselves

Along with plans for rationalizing services, there has been a second important strand in official thinking about ways of cutting the cost of health care. Since the mid-1970s the Department of Health has become increasingly enthusiastic about what it calls 'prevention'. At first sight, any shift from looking for cures to looking at causes must be welcome. The problem has been that the way what is making us ill has been defined and the solutions proposed intensify the victim-blaming way of thinking.

The first initiative in the recent vogue for prevention came
from what may seem an unlikely place. In 1975 the government asked the House of Commons Expenditure Committee
to investigate the money-saving possibilities of preventive
medicine. In 1977 the Committee published the results of its
investigation:

> We have been convinced by our enquiry that substantial human and
> financial resources would be saved if greater emphasis were to be put
> on prevention. This is not just a theoretical conclusion; it is literally a
> matter of life and death. Our recommendations cover organisation,
> advertising, finance and *last but not least self help*.[11] [our emphasis]

The Department of Health was already on the bandwagon. Its
booklet *Prevention and Health: Everybody's Business*[12] spelt out
the new thinking:

> A great battle has been won, and at first sight the victory seems
> complete, but a second look shows a different picture. More people can
> expect to live longer than in previous generations, but many still die
> prematurely or are for many years of their life dogged by avoidable ill
> health. We all need to be more aware of how we can help ourselves, our
> families and the community as a whole to avoid illnesses and their
> consequences.

Health economists, both in Britain and in the United States,
had been studying the mounting costs of health care. Looking
at the costs and benefits, they began to recognize, rightly, that
all this spending was not resulting in lower mortality rates or
greater life expectancy. Prevention seemed an obvious alternative.

The accent on prevention was encouraging, but from the very
beginning of its recent reappearance in official thinking the
emphasis was on ways of changing our *individual* behaviour. The
government, still under Labour, was quite explicit that prevention is a personal not a political matter. Its official response to
the Expenditure Committee's White Paper *Prevention and
Health*, published later in 1977,[13] included the statement:

A rising standard of living, which has contributed to the improvement of the population's health in the past, cannot be expected to improve the position with regard to the modern scourges . . . In fact, unless habits can be changed further, increases in the standard of living may result in an increased prevalence of these diseases.

At a time when many other government departments and quangos were being squeezed, the budget of the Health Education Council grew by leaps and bounds. The message which emerged was clear. We should all change our health behaviour and begin looking after ourselves.

Then in their deliberations the policy-makers turned their minds to who is getting ill, who is failing to look after themselves. The answer was as ever. The White Paper *Prevention and Health* raised what it described as the 'problem of communicating effectively with people in social class four and five'. These people became the special target of much of the health educators' efforts.

When the Conservatives came to office they reinforced the new message, adding their own subtle twist. It is not just that people could be healthier if they looked after themselves better, but that people get ill through being anti-social and irresponsible. *Care in Action*,[14] the Conservative government's major policy statement on health, published in 1981, began its chapter on prevention:

The prevention of mental and physical ill health is a prime objective and an area in which the individual has clear responsibilities. No one can wholly escape illness or injury, but there are plenty of risks to health which are in the individual's power to reduce or avoid. Too many endanger their health through ignorance or social pressures.

In a few deft logical steps the ill health that working-class people struggle against has been rendered a product of their own inadequacies.[15] For women the prevention message – while containing partial truths – is a recipe for double guilt. By providing the wrong food, smoking during pregnancy and delaying antenatal care, women are not only failing themselves but damaging their families too.

Doubting medicine

Although to some extent there is a criticism of high-technology medicine implicit in the new emphasis on prevention, it has been welcomed and encouraged by many sections of the medical profession, particularly the Royal College of General Practitioners and the Royal College of Physicians. The approach of the doctors has in many ways reflected the government's life-stylism, but there has sometimes been less victim blaming and more preparedness to take account of some societal causes of ill health. The Royal College of Physicians has been particularly active in pressing the government to ban tobacco advertising. Sir Douglas Black, its president, also chaired the working group on *Inequalities in Health*.

Although doctors are slow to share their doubts in public, there are signs that for some sections of medicine the present crisis in health care runs deeper than a shortage of resources. The shortage of money, caused by the conflicting pressures of government expenditure cuts and an ever growing bill for drugs and technology, is raising more basic questions. In the last decade there has been doubt on two levels. The first is a gradual realization that all the research effort of the past twenty years is not coming up with remedies for the major diseases. The second has to do with the contradiction between the new ideas emerging about the causes of some modern diseases and medicine's present model of the workings of the human body. The crisis in funding is highlighting a deeper crisis in the medical model. The answers are not emerging by looking inside. There is, on the other hand, increasing evidence that looking outside may give us more clues about the causes of illness. Heart disease and some chronic conditions are being increasingly linked to the rush and bustle of modern life. But the relationship between the outside and the inside implied by these new insights is in contradiction with medicine's present understanding of the nature of disease. Directing attention back on to ourselves is one way of coping with the weaknesses in medicine's paradigm. The new enthusiasm for personal responsibility serves to divert our attention from medicine's failure to deliver according to its promises.

The other way medicine has begun to deal with the problems in its own model is to squash the hundreds of ways in which our social experience can affect our bodies into one concept, *stress*. Stress is being squeezed into medicine's model as another kind of germ, another harmful pathogen. Like cholesterol, too much is bad. There is little discussion of how one person's stress may be another's excitement and no distinction between the 'stress' of being a top executive and the 'stress' of being beaten up by your husband or the 'stress' of the production line, although these are likely to give rise to quite different problems.

A new mode of domination

Medicine's inner doubts may be on the increase, but this shows no sign of affecting its outward confidence. Despite the present interest in changing habits and behaviour, in some ways high-technology medicine has never had it so good. For increasingly it is being seen as the legitimate part of health care to receive state funding. Rehabilitation, convalescence and care are coming to be regarded more and more as the province of charity or the family. Meanwhile we are also being encouraged not to take minor ailments to the doctor. The latest advice is that we should go directly to the chemist instead, and buy our remedies over the counter. Speaking at the launch of an advertising campaign for chemists in March 1983, Kenneth Clarke, Minister of Health, called for 'sensible self-medication'.[16] Out of the crisis a new definition of our rights and responsibilities is emerging. The old 'We will take care of you from the cradle to the grave' is being replaced by new terms of reference for what health care is about.

It is becoming increasingly clear that the Department of Health does not regard its responsibility for care in the same way as it sees its responsibility for medical treatment. Innovations in care for the mentally handicapped and stroke patients are two areas where ministers have been quite explicit that charities have the primary role. In another speech in March 1983, this time encouraging voluntary organizations to get involved in stroke rehabilitation, Kenneth Clarke said quite clearly that there are no longer resources to provide proper care as well as treatment: 'The rehabilitation of stroke patients to the maximum possible extent both physically and most importantly socially is a lengthy and time-consuming process which the professional medical and nursing staff do not have the time to provide.' He evidently sees the NHS's obligations stopping short of proper rehabilitation. The tendency we pointed to in Chapter 5 of prioritizing medical intervention, while seeing other aspects of care as subsidiary, is becoming stronger all the time. This view coincides with the pattern of cuts. Health workers struggling against heavy work-loads and short staffing would not thank us for saying it, but the clinical aspects of health care are being preserved at the expense of everyday care.

The new definition of the role of the health service returns the responsibility for not getting sick and for the routine care of those who are ill to the family. Better-off people will cope by buying their varicose veins operations and signing up with the BUPA Well Woman clinic. They will have the money to convert their elderly relatives' homes so they can manage on their own. They will be able to afford someone from the local flats to shop and clean for them. Confident of the future, those who are not losing out as the crisis deepens will cheerfully embrace the 'look after yourself' philosophy. But for the majority of people the picture is very different. Most people will face a choice between abandoning their sick relatives to increasingly impoverished state institutions or bearing the strain and worry of coping with them at home. Women forced out of the labour market will find

themselves imprisoned deeper in the home as community support services diminish. In such a situation the idea of being
positive about our own health seems like a sick joke.

Those who are waiting for the health service to collapse
completely before the crisis is officially declared will wait in vain.
Bone marrow transplants will still be done. Whole body scanners
will still be bought. The ambulance will still arrive at the motor-
way pile-up. Sophisticated medicine has powerful defenders.
And because the technology is expensive and the work labour-
intensive it is unlikely the state will abandon it to the private
sector. It is the quality of routine everyday care that is deteriorating. It is a quiet crisis. The suffering is very private. An elderly
man dressed in his best suit sits at home in a cold hallway all day
for an ambulance which never comes. Wearily, a single mother
washes the sheets of her twenty-five-year-old doubly incontinent
son, unable to remember the last time he allowed her to sleep
through the night. No one sees their silent tears. They are not
headline news.

10 New Opportunities

It is often said that a good health care system should prevent, cure and care. We have seen that prevention is far more than a matter of early medical intervention, but to the extent that the NHS normally recognizes this – by telling us to change our life-style – it does more harm than good by obscuring the social origins of so much ill health. We have seen that medicine has few ways of completely taking away illnesses which would not have got better by themselves. Medical intervention has the first call on NHS resources, while its actual contribution to making people better often goes unevaluated. We have seen that, while much of the NHS is to do with caring rather than curing, this aspect of its work is undervalued and under-resourced.

With more money and changed values, there is within the NHS the potential for much more highly developed health *care*, from improving techniques for pain relief to providing a home life and supportive environment for the very elderly sick. For better health care we do not have to wait for science to deliver its next miracle cure. By applying the knowledge and experience already existing among health workers, the many aspects of health care which are about relieving suffering and helping people get back to normal life could be vastly improved today.

But the problem with our present health care system is not just that it has got its priorities wrong. In the Introduction we asked a crude question: Is medicine helping or hindering in the struggle for better health – whose side is it on? We have seen some of the ways in which it colludes with the forces that make us sick; how, by telling us it can cure us, it diverts attention from what in our lives could be making us ill; how, by keeping us in fear and ignorance, it prevents us from asking questions about what is making us sick; how it makes us feel our illness is our own fault; how its science gives legitimacy to the view that the problem is in nature rather than society; how the practice which that science reinforces makes concrete this mystification. This is surely class medicine. From government policy and health authority planning to our encounters in the surgery and with the X-ray machine, a view of health and illness is being reproduced daily which obscures the possibility that the key to better health might lie in social change. Our struggles – for better living standards, better childcare, less oppressive sexual relations, against exhausting and demeaning work, against racism, against violence against women – are undermined.

The NHS was fought for before the Second World War by socialists committed to a medicine which, freed from market forces, would repair the health-damaging consequences of the harsh society outside. Today we have a form of financing health care which has partially removed it from the market and lifted the terrible financial worries which ill health can bring. It was a victory and it is to be defended. Even in the present bleak situation, we should value the partial victories which our struggles of the last few years to defend the NHS have also brought. If it had not been for the spate of hospital occupations in 1979, 1980 and 1981, the cuts in the NHS would have been even more savage. But today's health service is still shaped by market forces – particularly the pharmaceutical industry – and still deeply tied into ruling values. The role of the NHS today is as much to bolster as to mitigate the health-damaging society.

As the crisis deepens, the health service becomes less adequate to our needs, while the pressures which destroy our health increase. While those in work must produce faster, there is less and less those out of work can do. Women's isolation in the home is increasing. On the streets violence against women and racism continue unabated. Fewer pensioners can afford to heat their homes. More houses are falling into disrepair. People feel more hopeless, more fearful, more isolated. Now the cries of 'look after yourself', 'It's all your own fault' become more strident, while the claims for the health-restoring applications of the technology of the new era become more exaggerated.

But times of crisis are also times of opportunity. One of the reasons why medicine is now being widely questioned is that resisting the restructuring has made us think about what is wrong and how things might be. We have been influenced by the health economists who have pointed out the ineffectiveness of medicine, even if we reject their solutions. In fighting against hospital closures we have had first-hand experience of what medicine seeks to preserve and what it sees as dispensable. We have found out what people think about hospitals and doctors, what it is about them that they want saved and what they want changed. In work-ins, workers and patients have begun to change their relationships with each other and introduce new services. The rationalization schemes have brought to our attention the factory values at the heart of hospital management theory. Workers' resistance to bonus schemes and other productivity drives and their struggle for better wages has heightened our consciousness of how hospitals damage workers' health. The new spate of health education propaganda has made the 'victim-blaming' way of thinking more easily identifiable and has made us think about what kinds of health education we would prefer. The women's movement, in bringing patriarchal attitudes into the open, has also begun to spell out how health care might be more appropriate to our needs. If there were no crisis there might be less debate and less possibility of change.

Our present criticisms of health care do not come simply from the crisis in the NHS, but from the broader social movements which have spoken out about the way doctors reinforce dominant values. The critique of the intimate encounter, as well as the recognition that shame and secrecy are part of our oppression and that sharing problems is healing, has come out of a decade of discussion in women's consciousness-raising groups. The movement against the introduction of NHS charges for people from overseas has highlighted the nature of everyday racism in the NHS. In rejecting medicine's 'It's just your age', the pensioners' movement is refusing to accept purely biological explanations for problems which are also social in origin. The health and safety at work movement has documented many doctors' readiness to take the side of the employer in underplaying the dangers of work hazards. The network of women's refuges has discovered how many doctors are slow to help battered women to take action against their husbands. The rape crisis centres have reported doctors' collusion with police victim blaming. Tenants' associations have discovered how District Medical Officers often collude in undermining demands for better housing by restricting the grounds for rehousing on medical grounds.

In this section of the book we have tried to piece together the picture which emerges from all these struggles. In Part Three we want to explore the implications for how health care might be. Could it be different? Can we conceive of it *on our side*?

What is possible to imagine is limited by our experience. How we would like things to be can never be much more than a mirror image of our criticism of how things are. This is why it is dangerous to be too rigid about our prescriptions for the future. New forms of organization and new relationships between people are made in the course of struggle. To some extent all movements for change involve an act of faith. Nevertheless, looking at a view of what is possible can stimulate discussion of what should be changed. Thinking about how things might be in the future can help us clarify what it is we are fighting for now.

Part Three

On Our Side

11   Health Is Struggle

Where does good health come from?

We have seen that medicine does not have the power to bring us better health. It can relieve symptoms. It can help in the management of acute crises of long-term illnesses. It can cure some conditions. It does save lives, although perhaps fewer than we imagine. And in other instances it can prolong life even when it is not able to overcome the illness. But it cannot alter our susceptibility to illness or our liability to chronic conditions. Even if a child only has a permanent runny nose, there is very little the doctor can do. Medicine cannot stop the recurrence of the headache, the chronic constipation, the backache, the arthritis which drags us down. It has no treatment to improve our general resistance to infections and other illnesses or to alter our chances of getting cancer. If we are run down, it cannot run us up.

Health is sometimes described in very abstract terms. Vera talks of lacking 'a complete feeling of wellbeing about myself'. The World Health Organization's often quoted definition of health speaks of 'a state of complete physical, mental and social wellbeing, not merely an absence of disease and infirmity'. The concept takes on a rather mystical quality. But what we want is not really hard to grasp. We want fewer chronic and recurrent illnesses, less cancer and heart disease, less depression and anxiety. Of course we cannot hope to abolish illness,[1] but the important point about the class pattern of health and illness we discussed in Chapter 1 is that it is the evidence of how much unnecessary ill health most people face. The level of health presently enjoyed by the people at the top of British society should not be seen as an absolute standard, but it is at least an indicator of how much better our health could be if our lives were different. Remember the size of the class differences: the top civil servants with a quarter the rate of heart attacks of men at the bottom of the Whitehall hierarchy; twice the level of chronic illness among people in social class five compared with social class one; levels of chronic depression among working-class women five times greater than that among middle-class women. That's a lot of unnecessary illness we could do without.

One of the purposes of this book is to point out that doing something about improving health is less the province of science than of politics. Our problem is not that we lack the knowledge or the research evidence which hold the key to better health. There is no *scientific* reason why we should not all enjoy the standard of health at present only a minority experience. Top people tend more to be well because they have the preconditions, like feeling in control of your life, enjoying your work and having somewhere decent to live, which any reasonable society should offer everyone. But, as the interviews in Part One showed, between us and less illness stands a society which is destructive of the health of most people. Thinking about the route to better health takes us back to old questions without easy answers: How do we say 'no' to unemployment? How do we fight for better housing and working conditions? How do we organize against oppression? How do we begin to take control of our lives? How can we resist those who profit from our ill health? How can we develop a society organized around meeting human needs rather than serving the dynamic of capital? There are no short cuts.[2]

Being aware of health and illness heightens our consciousness of all that damages us. But then there comes a point where that consciousness dissolves back into everyday life. Trying to separate the bits of our lives which are specifically to do with health becomes impossible. What we need for our health is mainly what we want anyway: fulfilling work; time for recreation and for domestic work, including looking after children; the resources to afford holidays, decent food and dry, spacious housing. We want safe places for children to play; clean air to breathe; freedom from sexism and racism and an environment which is not hostile to us. We want friendship, companionship, quality, autonomy, excitement without exhaustion, relaxation without boredom. The struggle for health is not separate from all the other struggles we are involved in as tenants, trade unionists, anti-nuclear or anti-racist campaigners, feminists or socialists.

Being conscious of health issues may lead to some stronger emphases in what we fight for. But for the most part, wanting to improve our lives is not different from wanting to improve our health. Sometimes people say 'Oh, the unions should do more about health and safety at work and not concentrate so much on wages.' But this is to make a false divide. For as long as the good things of life, like food and housing and holidays, have to be bought on the private market, incomes will remain crucial to our health. Obviously to be successful our struggle must be stronger and extend into more areas of life. We need to look more carefully at issues to do with the quality of our lives than we do at present, and thinking about health helps us do that. Being conscious of how exhaustion contributes to being run down strengthens our resolve to fight overtime and bonus schemes, for instance. And recognizing the damage done by alienated and monotonous work encourages us to reject more boring, low-paid jobs as the politicians' answer to unemployment. But, equally, a narrow definition of health can sometimes handicap us. We should not have to prove a job is dangerous, for instance; if it is boring we should not have to do it day in day out. We should not have to prove the flat is damp; if we don't like it we should not have to live in it. The fight for health is as much about wages as about safety conditions, as much about saying no to productivity deals as about accident prevention. It is as much about how an estate is planned as about lead pollution, as much about women having control over their own lives as about eating the right vitamins in pregnancy.

Collective action

Most of the time most people do not have a choice about whether to be involved in fighting back. The struggle is there all the time. We are continually caught up in a round of daily battles, with the boss, with the social security, with the landlord, with the council. Those who are prepared to see our health suffer while their interests are pursued will squeeze us until we resist, cutting wages, cutting benefits and pensions, leaving repairs undone. But often we are fighting on our own. One way of looking at illness is to see it as the cost of that resistance. We bear in our bodies the cost of an unequal struggle.

Each of the people interviewed in Part One was acutely aware of the personal costs of individual struggle. Andrew Tree was exhausted from bearing the brunt of the fight for a safe working environment. Baden Gough recognized that his heart attacks were linked to the enormous burden he was carrying as one of his factory's main trade union negotiators. Ruth linked her illness to her sense of powerlessness and frustration. Shan's illness followed a period when she was the only militant shop steward left. But each of the eight had also been sustained by collective action and saw this as the primary route to change. A strike at Andrew Tree's plant brought new safety regulations. Joint action by the Coventry temporary tenants, backed by the Coventry Trades Council, got over a hundred families, including Les Bennett's, rehoused. Vera's tenants' association got buses re-routed from a street where they were hazardous because they blocked the road. Shan emphasizes that, whatever the weaknesses of the union, without it, as she was in the second sweat-shop, you are even more exploited. We may not have a choice about whether to resist or not, but to some extent we have a choice about the *form* of that resistance, particularly whether we do it on our own or with other people. Vera says, 'What *is* in our power is to try to collect together.' Through joint action we take individualized resistance out of our bodies into collective struggle.

Collective action can be much more effective than individual action, and moreover the experience of collectivity and solidarity can itself be health-engendering, counteracting loneliness and powerlessness. Vera describes how her tenants' association got the buses rerouted:

We won on the buses. That was direct action. That was very beauti-ful. There were people who didn't know each other – who had seen each other vaguely – standing together. They had never done anything so obviously against the law like that. It was just after I had Kimmy, and I was beginning to walk again on my frame. We were all standing in the road, black and white. The neighbouring tenants' association came to join us because they said 'Your problem is our problem.' For a week we just barricaded the road. The bus drivers joined the line too.

On the same day as you were feeling low and not able to do the washing up or face the repetitive grind, you can stand on that barricade for hours. It gives you that energy. But it is more than that. It does feed that part of you which is getting blunted so much. You suddenly gain confidence. It goes. It always goes. But the thing is that you do not lose that moment.

Vera stresses that what was important about the action was not just the outcome – getting the buses rerouted – but the process, the experience of coming together, the feelings of closeness and confidence. This is a point that people involved in action to change things make over and over again. In the process of fighting back we can glimpse the values – the collectivity, the democratic decision-making, the caring and sharing, the new kinds of relationships between women and men and white and black – which we would like to assert more widely. These ways of relating to each other are to some extent the preconditions of our own health.

Health is about struggle, at home, at work, in our relations with each other, wherever we are. We cannot rely on policy-makers to protect us. It has to do with remaking our connections with each other, asserting our power, feeling our own strength and finding the energy to act. This is one of the reasons why, although we are a long way from the heady days of 1968, some of us still hope for revolutionary change. Many of the changes we need cannot be given to us. No government can ban loneliness or outlaw racist feelings. The new kinds of social relations we want are made in the course of resistance. The language of revolution seems silly and outmoded. But if ever there were a case for wholesale change, thinking about health makes it. We need fundamental change everywhere: in the organization of work and home life, in what products are made and the processes of their manufacture, in how looking after children and older people is shared, in the planning of cities, in what we eat and how that food is produced, in our relations with each other and our feelings about ourselves. The list is endless. The healthy life is not compatible with capitalism.

The role of health care

So if it seems that medicine has very little to do with our general standard of health, what is health care for? What can we expect of it?

The answer is threefold. First we need it to heal us, where healing is possible, to mend our broken bones, to help us survive life-threatening bouts of illness, to relieve chronic conditions. Second, we need it to care for us while we are either temporarily ill or permanently infirm. And, thirdly, we need it on our side in the wider struggle for better health. This is the link between health and health care. The health service cannot itself give us better health, but, as we have seen, it can help or hinder us in identifying and challenging what is making us ill. We spent a lot of Part Two looking at the role of medicine in reproducing ways of thinking which undermine our confidence in understanding our own bodies and distract us from the social origins of our ill health. One of the struggles within the NHS must be to challenge these ways of thinking and introduce ideas and practices which help us in the wider fight for better health.

It is often said by liberal and radical health workers alike that because the causes of ill health and the roads to better health lie outside of the health service, it is the responsibility of others – trade unions in the food industry, consumer groups or whoever – to fight for the changes we need. In fact it is now widely acknowledged at the most senior level of medicine, including the Royal Colleges, that doctors cannot be held responsible for providing better health. But all these people cannot let themselves off the hook quite that easily. For, while in the outside world our health is damaged, the health service carries on getting in the way of our understanding of what is damaging us. It is in the power of health workers to challenge the present dominant attitudes. We need new ideas and practices in the health service which remake the connection with the society that makes us sick. Instead of ignoring the causes of illness, excluding them, or turning them back upon ourselves, we need health care which reinforces and strengthens our consciousness of what we are up against and our will to fight it.

Recognizing that the struggle for better health happens primarily *outside* the health service is an absolute precondition of getting right what contribution health care cannot and can make. But we are not going to prescribe here the wider changes needed to improve our health. This is partly because if it were to be a revolutionary prescription, there are many other books about, and ways of understanding, the processes of social change. And if it were a reformist prescription the list of reforms would be very long, covering food policy, public health, housing, employment, unemployment, transport, nuclear weapons, and would seem rather unrealizable as things are. It is also because we do not want to collude with the 'It is nothing to do with the health service' brigade. We are focusing firmly on health *care* – on what goes on in clinics, hospitals and surgeries – because it could be very different, and those differences could in turn make a difference to broader struggles for social change.

How different the health service will become depends largely on how strong the broader social movement is. At times when there is energy, excitement and confidence in the movement for change in society as a whole, the possibilities for change within the health service will be greater. What is happening inside health care and outside of it might interact. Health workers, through their practice, could strengthen the wider movement, while this movement gave strength and confidence to forces for change within health care. Even now there is opposition within the health service. It is too hard to envisage in detail how a whole society might be different, but it is possible to conceive of how health care might be. And that sense of future possibilities can serve our present struggle.

Roots of change

In Part Two we described dominant ways of thinking within the health service. Every day and at every level in the NHS these are being resisted. The health service unions have grown enormously in the last decade. In 1970 few health workers were in a union. Now over 600,000 of the one million NHS staff are unionized. And co-ordination between unions has grown too, particularly in the past two or three years. As well as fighting for better wages and conditions, the unions are resisting the high-productivity management style and cuts and closures in needed services. Without the unions there is no doubt that the health service would have faced even more brutal cuts in funding. As well as resisting resource cuts, the unions act as a moderating influence on the NHS's almost paramilitary hierarchy. Doreen Walters has worked as a hospital cleaner for twenty years. Now she is a shop steward:

They used to treat us as if we didn't exist. What they forget is that it is just as important to how the operation turns out that I have done a good job of cleaning the floor as it is that the surgeon puts his knife in the right place. Now since we have had the union and have sat down with them at the negotiating table, they treat us with a bit more respect and dignity. God bless our great trade union movement.

Paramedical workers are challenging medicine's domination in all kinds of ways. During strikes and industrial action the media scorn the shop stewards' committees who presume to challenge management claims about which patients are genuine emergencies. But to these negotiations health workers, particularly operating department assistants, bring years of experience and knowledge. No one pretends these decisions are easy. But the discussion is rarely about borderline cases. The definition of an emergency is always very broad, and health workers can tell when the surgeon is obviously trying to disguise a routine case as an emergency. This is the sharp end of health workers' challenge to medical expertise. Groups like the Radical Midwives' Group, the Radical Nurses' Group, and the Radical Health Visitors' Group also challenge medical dominance in health care. Organized in the tradition of the women's movement, these groups have spoken out on issues like the medicalization of childbirth and have set up mutual support groups strengthening each other in their personal struggles at work. Recently the style of the Radical Nurses' Group has been taken into some union branches, extending the role of the union to personal support for members in the everyday challenges of their work.

Throughout the health service, health workers also struggle individually to challenge the medical hierarchy and factory values and to improve the care they give. The young nursing auxiliary in the mental handicap hospital causes trouble taking too long to dress the middle-aged men. He has been trying to find them suits to fit. The ward orderly risks the dislike of the charge nurse by pointing out the danger of bedsores if elderly people spend all day in their wheelchairs. The staff nurse confronts the nursing manager. The patients will be at risk on her ward unless the number of night staff is increased. The junior doctor insists to her consultant that a patient cannot be sent home yet. The health education officer refuses to distribute a patronizing leaflet for the elderly on hypothermia. To all these people the personal costs are high. Saying no is not easy in the health service, just as it is not easy to resist authority in any other part of our society.

The challenge to medical dominance and demands for improvements in the quality of care have come as much from outside the health service as within it. The women's movement has led the way in asserting our right to control our own bodies. Women's groups have helped us recognize that there are common patterns in our personal experiences of medicine, and have given us strength to challenge doctors. Self-help groups, self-examination groups, women's health courses and handbooks have helped us to appropriate knowledge we had previously been denied. Particularly in the fields of fertility control, antenatal care and childbirth, what women want has been powerfully stated and has become widely acknowledged. As a result, even Conservative ministers have been known to criticize production-line antenatal clinics, and practices within the health service are changing all the time. In particular the introduction of new approaches to childbirth within some NHS hospitals is an encouraging sign of the impact of a social movement which began with small groups of women meeting in consciousness-raising groups.

The atmosphere created by the women's health movement has given rise to a far more widespread questioning of medicine. Shan, Vera and Ruth describe how they asked questions when they shouldn't have asked questions and said no to treatments they were expected to accept. Many of our intimate encounters are confrontations requiring at least as much courage as standing on the picket line. Vera describes what she calls 'the individual struggle from the bed': 'It is getting people to realize that you are not just a piece of meat, you are a person. If you spread that feeling around the ward, that is an amazing thing to happen.'

Three principles

Vera goes on to say 'That's not enough. We've got to build more. At the moment, however, I don't know how you do that.' Neither do we – except to point out that a different health service will be built on the basis of all these tiny actions, developing them and drawing them together.

Changes at the policy level – formal decisions taken by the government, the Department of Health or health authorities – could help a lot. The health service desperately needs more money and a different decision-making structure for a start. But we cannot rely on new people coming into power with better policies, for a number of reasons. First, the record of the last Labour government was poor. As we explained in Chapter 6, today's high-productivity policies wrapped up in the rhetoric of 'priorities' were dreamed up while the Labour government was in office. Second, whatever the political will, you cannot legislate for people to relate to each other in different ways, to bring new attitudes into their practice, or to abolish informal power structures. Attitudes and practices are changed on the ground, mainly through individual encounters and through the influence of social movements. Third, if the policy-makers want to introduce more progressive policies, how they get implemented will depend on local enthusiasm for putting them into action, in turn a reflection of the strength of the movement within the health service.

In the following chapters we offer a framework for discussing what building on our existing strengths might mean. It is not a list of policy proposals, or a list of demands, or a collection of good practices. It is more of an agenda, a list of questions rather than answers. We look at other forms of healing and ask how the NHS might open up to them. We try to bring the term 'oppositional practice' down to earth. We talk of a new medicine and what it might be like. We look at how the caring side of the health service's work could be improved. We list the issues that manifesto writers and policy-makers should address. And we imagine what a health centre offering appropriate health care might be like.

No health care system can give us health, but what the NHS offers us could be far more appropriate to our needs. We can hope for three things of it: that it puts itself behind the struggle for better health; that it does all it can to improve the quality of the experience of being ill, of being disabled and of dying; and that, recognizing the limitations of orthodox medicine, it draws upon the widest range of healing knowledge to make available to us whatever skills there are to help us get better. These three principles, of opposition, of care and of healing, form the basis of the new approach we argue for.

CARE ON OUR TERMS

Caring for people is labour-intensive. To look after people well is time-consuming. It cannot be done by machines, and it cannot be done against the clock. All of which means that health care will always consume a high proportion of the total labour of any society. Like all work it should be properly paid. There is no way round it; good health care is expensive.

If we had the kind of health care we want, some savings could be made by better control of the production and consumption of drugs. Taking the production of drugs out of the sphere of private profit would be essential. New ways of meeting needs for which drugs are presently used and more careful prescribing could further reduce the drugs bill. More careful evaluation of specific diagnostic and treatment technologies might save some money too. But it could equally well cost more. A policy of putting resources into unequivocally beneficial medical interventions could increase the number of hip replacements and people being given kidney dialysis, for instance. All in all, it would be a serious mistake to assume that a health service which more carefully evaluated the role of medicine and put more effort into everyday health care, with properly paid health workers, would be cheaper. There is no way round the fact that good health care needs far more resources than at present the NHS receives.

At the moment Britain gets its health care on the cheap. Gross national product is not necessarily the best way of looking at a country's resources. It does not include a measure of domestic labour, or of the human resources lying idle through unemployment. And it includes a lot of 'product' – from armaments to junk food – that we would be better off without. Nevertheless GNP provides a crude measure. Britain spends only 5.4 per cent of its GNP on health care, just over half of the proportion spent in Sweden or the USA. In Europe only Greece and Austria spend a smaller percentage.[1] This is not to say that those countries spending a high proportion of their GNP on health care necessarily do it better. They waste a lot of money on the administration of health insurance, and, particularly in the USA, it is widely acknowledged that there are too many operations and too many diagnostic tests.[2] But the GNP figures are an indicator of the low priority Britain gives to health care. Like growing food, rearing children and building houses, looking after sick people is a basic part of human life and deserves to be properly resourced.

It is not a question of spending three or five per cent a year more on the NHS, as the Labour party advocates. The scale of additional resources required would be much greater. What is needed is a whole new way of looking at how the caring work in society gets done. At the moment it is either done in hospital or by people – almost always women – temporarily or permanently giving up a large part of their lives to care for relatives. We need new ways of sharing out the work. Just as childcare is beginning to be recognized as something in which society should assist, caring for ill friends and relatives should be seen in the same way. Just as we want better maternity and paternity leave, better working arrangements allowing time off in school holidays and when children are sick, we also need to fight for a recognition by employers and society that we have a right to take time off and to adjust our working hours to care for the people we are close to. For those who choose to look after the long-term ill or disabled, there should be a living income.

Choice

Being ill at home or looking after a sick, elderly or mentally handicapped person could be such a different experience if it were not combined with poverty and isolation, and if there were proper back-up services. It is possible for the most severely disabled people to live independently if they have full-time assistants to look after them. Caring for a mentally handicapped person can be greatly helped by laundry and incontinence services, regular relief for the carer to go out, easy access to transport and a centre where the mentally handicapped person can go during the day for company and stimulation.

Quite frail elderly people can continue to live on their own – if they want to – if their houses are adapted so it is easy for them to get round, to get to the toilet and in and out of the bath. They need to be visited regularly by home nurses and have someone to do the shopping, or to take them to the shops, help with housework and preparing meals. There is nothing wrong with being sent home early from hospital if the home nursing service is very good and there is someone to bath, cook and shop for you.

But no one – neither cared for nor carers – should be forced into a bitter or resented caring relationship for lack of adequate alternatives. What we need is choice. At present people are caught between impoverished institutional care or coping at home with very little back-up. Relations who choose institutional care often have to cope with the guilt this induces, while looking after dependent relatives at home can put such a severe strain on relationships that marriages often break up. The number of mothers of mentally handicapped children who are coping on their own is striking. The choice should be between well-resourced home care and appropriate care in hospital or small units staffed by health workers. Just as there is no reason in principle why home care should be grim, there is also no reason why being looked after by full-time health workers away from home should be a bad experience. There are many good reasons why it might not be appropriate for elderly, mentally ill, mentally handicapped, sick or disabled people to be looked after at home. They may be lonely. They may not get on with their families (this is particularly the case with mentally ill people, who may find that being with their families makes things worse) or may not wish to be dependent on them. Their families may not be able, or may not want, to look after them. Women should not be expected to sacrifice their jobs and lives outside the home to nurse dependent relatives unwillingly.

In general the conditions for making care away from home a good experience are quite straightforward. People want small units, not big institutions. Sometimes they want to get away and be in the country, but often they prefer to be near their homes in their own neighbourhoods. They want a homely atmosphere. They want privacy and autonomy and to be able to retain control of their decisions about their daily lives. They want stimulation and company. They want a say in how the place where they live is run and organized. They want people to relate to them, not as an extension of their sickness or disability, but in an ordinary way.

Good practice

Adequate care for people who are infirm or disabled would mean offering both well-resourced home-care support teams and small local units for care away from home. While policy-makers could provide a framework for such developments, many aspects of the new approach could not be legislated for. The policy-makers should insist, for instance, that all units are organized and run jointly by the people who work in and use them, but what forms this democracy should take could not be centrally determined.

Almost by definition, appropriate ways of meeting people's needs must develop from close contact with them. Attitudes change by interaction between people, not by decree. Policy-makers could unblock some obstacles, like the obstacle of lack of money and the obstacle of rigid hierarchies which do not permit new ideas and sap the energy of the people at the bottom. Curbing the power of medicine and introducing democratic decision-making, in which health workers and users of the health service had an equal say, would enable the ideas and suggestions of patients, relatives and health workers directly involved in caring to emerge. Those charged with running the health service at central or local level can also look for and nurture ways of doing things, projects and initiatives which seem to embody the kind of approach we need. Even today there is no shortage of good ideas and good practice. With resources and encouragement these could be built on far more widely. Money should be available to fund new local initiatives which could become models for care elsewhere. These initiatives should be paid for by the NHS, while workers and users retain control.

There are dozens of good schemes to get mentally handicapped people out of big hospitals into small local units, the vast majority of which are on ice because the government has not matched its commitment in principle to 'community care' with anywhere near the money it needs. There are model projects where severely physically disabled, mentally ill or mentally handicapped people are enabled to live in small groups and retain control of their lives. And in hospitals all over the country there are health workers worming away individually to make things better. Outside the health service, too, there are many examples of better practice in care, like the Rudolf Steiner communities for the mentally handicapped, and hospices which offer an entirely different approach to the care of dying people.

Often initiatives like these and many others, run by charities, offering a different style of care have been set up outside the health service because they are too labour-intensive, and thus too expensive for the NHS's shoe-string budget. If the health service were to say it could no longer afford the best available drugs there would be an outcry, yet for too long we have accepted that the health service provides second-class care for its long-stay patients. In medicine we hear a lot about the pursuit of excellence. The teaching hospitals are known as 'centres of excellence'. But where is excellence in *care*? In every neighbourhood we want our own centres of excellence where the old, the frail, the severely disabled, the mentally ill and the mentally handicapped are assisted in pursuing their lives, their work and their friendships on their own terms.

Disabled people say that they are disabled not only by the bits of their bodies that are missing or do not work properly, but by society, which denies them the resources and the support to get on with their lives. On the television news, as the last item there is often a sentimental spot, which from time to time is filled with a piece about a new kind of technology that will transform the lives of the paraplegic, of the deaf or of the blind. Last night it showed a wheelchair-bound woman who had not walked for eleven years taking her first steps with the aid of a frame. A new kind of electrical stimulation had brought the feeling to her legs. Every time we scream back at the telly 'But who will pay?' Aiding disabled living is surely one area where high technology is appropriate and can transform lives. But there are still hundreds of devices, like electric wheelchairs able to go up and down kerbs, which would make life easier for people, which they do not have because they cannot afford them and the health service will not pay for them. With new priorities, the very sophisticated technology now going into the manufacture of armaments could be redirected. The modern technology of weaponry involves devices which are extremely sensitive to human responses. This knowledge could be applied to helping people live, rather than devising even more ingenious ways of killing.

Radically improving the quality of the experience of illness or disability is not something that must await new discoveries or scientific breakthroughs. The knowledge, the skill, the technology and the will to care for people well exist now. We need a health care system which will mobilize that caring. We want encouragement and solidarity for all those health workers who are at present fighting on their own and against the odds for better care. We want medicine in its place, so that nurses and occupational therapists and ambulance drivers and all the other health workers directly involved, as well as patients and relatives, can have their say about what is needed and how services should be organized and developed. And we want the resources to realize their dreams.

OPPOSITIONAL PRACTICE

Being within the state, we need to oppose the state from within.
In and Against the State[3]

How can a health service help us stand up to what is making us ill? How could health workers help remake or reinforce the links in our consciousness between our health and the social forces which act upon it? How can we get rid of the myths? What will replace them?

Out of the dark

The first step is feeling more confident about our own bodies. People are less likely to challenge what is making them ill if they are anxious or fearful about their own health or feel alienated from their bodies. Taking control of our own bodies builds our confidence in tackling wider issues. We have a right to information, straight talking, honest answers and explanations. We want more egalitarian relationships with doctors and other health workers. For too long keeping us in the dark has been second nature. Doctors' feelings that they must protect us from painful knowledge are now out of date. Being fobbed off and left with unspoken worries and unanswered questions is far more painful. Over the past ten years the feeling that we don't like not knowing what is meant to be the matter with us, what the treatment involves or what the side effects might be has been most strongly articulated by the women's movement. Women's groups have also shown how it is possible to begin to take control of our bodies through learning about them, self-examination, asking questions, sharing our experiences with each other and getting support from each other for our encounters with medicine. But the desire to talk over how we feel, what the options are and what might be causing our problems goes far beyond the women's movement. Many, many women and men are fed up with being patronized and blamed. They want doctors and other health professionals to level with them. People don't want dos and don'ts and oughts, but they do want information on which to make up their own minds. The popularity of health courses and self-help handbooks for women and pensioners has shown that people want to learn about biology and physiology. They are interested in the arguments for and against whooping cough vaccination. They are interested in why what they call rheumatism the doctor calls arthritis. They want to know where cancer comes from and whether it can be cured.

It would be wrong to imply that the desire for information is universal. Lots of people are blocked off about their own health and bodies. Beginning to ask questions to try and understand what is happening to us sometimes means facing up to deep anxieties. People have very mixed feelings. Some don't want to know. We are not demanding that information that people find uncomfortable is crammed down patients' throats, but that health workers should be sensitive to what the people who come to see them want. The aim should be to change the atmosphere in society so that there is more knowledge and less fear among people in general. This should mean that people who might in the past have resisted finding out would find it easier to ask questions. As the momentum of a different approach to know-ledge sharing and action based on that knowledge grew, so people might choose more often to seek out advice and information rather than put up with half-conscious worries.

Vera points out that people do not want information if there is nothing useful they can do with it. Information and action are intimately linked:

> More people in the health service who have held the power have got to accept that people can know their bodies and themselves if they are given the confidence to think about it more than they are now allowed to. We need a greater awareness of our not-very-wellness and of what is causing it. But how can you expect that awareness to happen until there are structures in which we can do something about it? It is all very well to recognize what is happening to you, but it is a frustrating business when you feel powerless in altering and changing it. We need more information about our own bodies. But it has to be given in a way which gives us a sense of our own power. It has to be a positive thing, not a downer.

Looking at our lives

As well as information about drugs and diagnoses, we also want a new approach to exploring what is wrong with us. Health workers should help us look at our lives, working with us to construct an understanding of what is causing our complaints. In addition to using internal measures, pathology tests, X-rays and blood pressure readings, we want health workers to listen and to apply their experience and skills to working out with us where our problems are coming from and what might be done. We want encouragement to value our own insights.

Obviously this approach would not apply to all conditions. If someone has a broken leg the job is to get on with setting it rather than to sit round discussing the ins and outs of the accident. But for almost all chronic conditions and many long-term illnesses it is worth spending time looking at when it comes on and when it gets worse and what is happening in the rest of your life. We want an approach which takes *biography* as seriously as pathology.[4] This will not always bring solutions. It is often very difficult simply to disentangle the complex web of factors which are causing someone not to be well, let alone doing something about them. But looking at our lives is the beginning of remaking the connection between our illness and the social world.

The doctor's practice shapes our view of health and illness. By helping us to see the links between what is happening to us and the social forces we live among, by taking away the blame and helping us to look outwards not inwards, the health worker can help to dispel the myths that entangle us and to reinforce a different and more class-conscious way of looking at the world.

New forms of solidarity

In the individual encounter, suffering is personal. It belongs to us in a special way, but it also has its origins, as often as not, in circumstances which are common. The practice we need has to find a way of taking account of both, and of losing neither in the other. Mutual support groups are one way of retaining the focus on the problems faced by individuals while helping to build a common understanding of them. One of the most powerful lessons the women's movement has learned is that sharing our problems with others can give us strength to confront difficulties in our own lives. In the last few years this approach has spread rapidly, far beyond the women's movement.

There are already lots and lots of groups which provide support to people facing common difficulties. For instance, there are local women's groups and pensioners' groups, groups for parents who have suffered a cot death, groups for sufferers from epilepsy or psoriasis, and groups helping to deal with addictions, including smoking, eating, tranquillizers and alcohol. Some are very well established, others are far more tentative. Where there may now be one in every town, there could be one in every surgery or neighbourhood centre. In such groups we recognize that experiences we had seen as very personal can be very common. They are consciousness-raising. They can help us to get our problems in perspective and to work out what can be done about them. And they are a source of strength and confidence in doing battle with the rest of the world, whether it is the tobacco, the doctor, the boss, the husband or the social security. The mutual support group offers a different kind of solidarity from that of the trade union or the tenants' association. In the union we are all in it together, confronting the employer collectively. Mutual support groups are appropriate, on the other hand, where the political encounter is very personal. Occasionally these groups do become involved in collective confrontation, but for the most part they offer solidarity in what are almost inevitably individual struggles. Health workers could do far more to help to establish such groups, shifting the weight of effort away from the individual encounter into the beginnings of a collective way of responding to needs.

Of course, not all the groups at the moment look at things from the same perspective. And some of the perspectives might be ones we would want to argue with. Many weight-watching groups, for instance, deal with eating problems by getting people to lose weight in competition with each other and by making them feel guilty if they do not cut down; compulsive eating groups, on the other hand, do not assume it is good to be thin, and focus on why it is that women want to keep on eating. The latter approach has far more in common with the way of thinking we would like to see more widely established. It counters rather than reinforces sexist stereotypes that women must be thin, and looks to the causes of compulsive eating in women's oppression.

It offers at the same time a personal route for women concerned about their weight and a political perspective on the societal causes of compulsive eating.

Building a new health common-sense

The individual encounter with the sick person should be a learning experience, but in addition to this the health service has a broader role in helping us learn about health and illness. Of course in some ways we know far more about what is making us ill than many health professionals, at least at present. Mutual support groups have a role, too, in deepening that understanding. But the health service potentially does have massive resources for health education – not the victim blaming we have at the moment from the Health Education Council and many health education departments, but information to warn us and make us angry. People want to know about the dangers of pollution, of junk food or workplace hazards. They are interested in what research has been done on shiftwork or damp. The NHS should be creating a new kind of health common-sense, so that it becomes second nature for people to reflect on how their lives and their environment affect their health.

In Part Two of this book we looked at the power of present-day practice in the health service in shaping people's views of health and illness. A different practice based on a different view could be equally powerful, rupturing the smooth reproduction of the social relations which damage us. At the moment, taking a collective interest in health as often as not boils down to raising money for a whole body scanner. But if health care were different, our consciousness would be too. Thinking about collective dangers to health and how to fight them could become second nature. Just as it is now usual for people to wash their hands when they have been to the toilet, it might become everyday good sense to think: What additives are there in the food I am eating? Will the productivity scheme the management want to bring in increase the stress we are under? How will the plan to reroute the traffic in our area affect the lead in the air?[5]

There is also a role for health education in disseminating information about how our bodies work, what is known about the causes of illness, and about the conditions for being well. At the moment most health education serves the *status quo*. But it could be subversive. A redistribution of knowledge is a precondition for changing medicine and health care, as well as for opposing what is making us ill in the wider society.

Support for collective action

As well as supporting collective discussion, health workers can also give practical support to collective action. We need health workers who can advise on the safety of work processes, who can find out about the toxicity of chemicals, who will come to meetings and answer questions. We need health workers who will go to neighbourhood meetings and help design surveys to find out what illnesses people are suffering and whether they might be related to housing conditions. We need researchers, pharmacologists and epidemiologists who will help us identify workplace hazards.[6] We want health workers who will help us make the case for better housing or improved working conditions.[7] Health workers should be prepared to come out of their surgeries, hospitals and clinics to look for where people are fighting back and ask 'How can we help?' They should also be prepared to speak out, as they are now doing about nuclear weapons, on other issues which are equally crucial to our health. Doctors seem so strong and powerful and yet so often when their voices are needed, to condemn a drug or a new government policy, for instance, they say they cannot give their point of view because they fear they will not get another job or promotion. The point is not that health workers should martyr themselves but that they should see what they do in their jobs as an area of struggle. Their aim should be to establish that helping other people to contest the causes of ill health is a legitimate aspect of health care. It is a question of fighting for the idea that health care is just as much about assisting *groups* of people resist the forces that destroy their health – unions, tenants' associations or whoever – as about helping *individuals*, often unsuccessfully, to get better. No one pretends it is easy.

It's happening now

Our ideas about oppositional practice come from what is already happening inside the health service. Ethel speaks well of her doctor. She likes him because he listens, and because the surgery is friendly; she feels welcome and an equal. She likes the groups he has set up and she likes him because he fights back.

What I like about my doctor is he listens. When it is my turn he does not say 'Mrs Fraser!' sharply, he just nods me to come. The others waiting say 'Oh, you've got the nod.' I say 'I always get a nod.' And you can go and have five or six cups of tea in his surgery. There is an urn and a big tea pot. Another thing I like is that he has everything for children to play with. He has an afternoon for children and an afternoon for women that are expecting. The old doctor listened, but not like this one. This one listens until you have finished what you have got to say. He would help any person, whether they were black, white, green or blue. He is trying to get a permanent site for the gypsies and he fought for the nurses' pay.

Up and down the country, groups of health workers are developing ways of doing their jobs differently, trying to establish more equal relationships with patients, setting up mutual support groups and lending their weight to local struggles. A group of practices in Sheffield have work health advisers based in their surgeries. They talk to patients in the waiting area about where they work and what the processes are. They are building up a record system to help identify causes of illnesses which seem to occur unusually often. They organize meetings about particular health hazards and help shop stewards carry out their own health screening, such as hearing tests, with fellow workers.

At a practice in South London the doctors meet their patients in the waiting room, unless they specially ask to be seen in private. Other patients join in. Sometimes their advice can be as helpful as the doctors'. The patients can see their medical records. The waiting room becomes a meeting room in the afternoons and evenings. Health education workers run health courses, health clubs, and health buses, helping people to learn about their bodies, share experiences and build up confidence with doctors. Individual doctors give help to unions, tenants' associations and community groups. Others seek more equal relationships with their patients, allowing them to see their medical records. Some have taken a biographical approach for years. Developments in oppositional practice will come from these roots.

In 1931 Sylvia Pankhurst and Frank Bushnell, members of the Independent Labour Party, founded the Socialist Workers National Health Council. The aim was to conduct 'a campaign to teach people not to get used to the losses and sufferings from disease, *but to react against them*' (our emphasis). Their goal of encouraging people to refuse to see their suffering as natural or inevitable is as relevant today as it was in the 1930s. Health workers are up against a lot. But those with professional jobs, especially doctors, do have opportunities to decide whose side they are on. Those who want to think through their present practice might like to ask themselves:

1. Am I sharing my knowledge, or do I sometimes keep from people what I know? Am I encouraging people to take control over their own health, or do I make them feel guilty?

2. Do I listen to what patients want to tell me? Do I cut them short? Do I assume I can work out what is wrong without hearing them out? Do I ask *them* what is making them ill? Do I look at their illnesses in the context of their lives?

3. Am I helping or hindering people from understanding

what is making them ill? Do we discuss what might be causing their problems?

4. Do I explain the procedures I am undertaking? Do I offer patients options when there are several possible treatments? Am I realistic in what I tell patients about their illnesses and treatments? Do I take the side effects they report seriously?

5. How can I help people to recognize their common problems and give support to each other in contesting or coping with them? Am I trying to deal individually with problems which could be better explored collectively?

6. Could I do more to share my skills?

7. Where are people fighting back in my neighbourhood? How could health workers help?

8. Do I have colleagues who will back my practice? Where can I get support if what I do is challenged? How can I make links with others doing similar things?

A WIDER VIEW OF HEALING

Healing cannot be made discrete and tangible; it involves too many little kindnesses, encouragements, and stored up data about the patients' fears and strengths (all the things trivialised today as 'bedside manner'). It cannot be quantified: the midwife does not count the number of times she wiped the parturient women's forehead or squeezed her hand. Above all, it cannot be plucked out – as a thing apart – from the web of human relationships which connect the healer with those she helps.

Barbara Ehrenreich and Deirdre English[8]

Chapter 5, 'What can medicine do?', was written with the help of several doctors. To check it out from another perspective, we gave the draft to a colleague who works as a naturopath and osteopath. She was not happy with it. While broadly agreeing with our assessment of NHS medicine, she felt that by saying that medicine has not got the answers to many illnesses, particularly chronic conditions, we were implying that nothing could be done about them. As we went through the list of common illnesses she exclaimed over and over again: 'But there are other forms of healing for that condition!'

Going through the examples given in the chapter, she explained what she knew could be done for them:

No one has the answer to arthritis, but the pain can be relieved and the swelling reduced by cutting out certain foods. Acupuncture and internal and external use of the powerful herb comfrey can also help . . .

The basic answer to depression and anxiety does not lie in any kind of medication – orthodox or alternative – but effective calming herbs, like valerian, at least do not carry the danger of addiction . . .

Ulcerative colitis can be greatly relieved by a combination of diet, the application of hot and cold water, and herbs, particularly slippery elm. Although it is not always easy, looking at what is getting you down and trying to do something about it is also crucial in this condition . . .

Women's illnesses, from cystitis and thrush to pelvic inflammatory disease and chronic menstrual pain, can often be relieved with special combinations of herbs and diet. Acupuncture and hydrotherapy can help too. So can counselling and therapy.

Back pain can be greatly helped by osteopathy, a technique for manipulation of the bones, joints and muscles . . .

In life-long diabetes, insulin deserves the praise it gets, but the less serious diabetes which comes on in middle age can be controlled without insulin by changes in diet, as many orthodox doctors recognize . . .

High blood pressure is risky and does need to be brought down. But there are many ways other than tablets to do this, including changes in diet, exercise, meditation and looking at stress . . .

Over the past ten years there has been a massive growth in the popularity of what has come to be known as 'alternative medicine'. Some of these alternative practitioners – such as herbalists – belong to traditions dating back to the Middle Ages.[9] Naturopathy, whose therapies primarily involve changes in diet, and osteopathy were nineteenth-century developments of the popular healing tradition which existed in opposition to orthodox medicine and drew strongly on herbal remedies. Homeopathy, a system of treatment based on minute doses of substances which give rise to the symptoms of the disease in healthy people, was devised by Samuel Hahnemann in Germany in the late eighteenth century. By the mid-nineteenth century it was being practised in Britain. Acupuncturists have established themselves more recently, but the practice of acupuncture in China is centuries old.

At the same time there has been a complementary explosion in psychotherapy. Many of the kinds of therapy being practised in Britain have developed out of the American gestalt and encounter movements. Others have their roots more directly in psychoanalysis and in post-Freudian therapy, including Jungian and Reichian approaches. As well as offering an alternative to psychotropic drugs and mental hospitals, psychotherapy can be useful in relieving physical complaints.[10]

Rediscovery

From childhood most of us have been taught to dismiss, if not despise, other forms of healing. The healing lore of our great-grandmothers was seen as 'old wives' tales'. At best those who practised other methods were seen as quacks and cranks, at worst as con-men and charlatans. But as more and more people have sought the help of alternative practitioners, fragments of a different picture have begun to emerge. A friend had severe digestive problems and had been told she might have to have surgery. After a year of seeing a naturopath, who suggested a major change in diet, she is eating almost normally and enjoying life again. Another finds relief from shoulder pain with an osteopath. A woman finds her asthma has virtually disappeared with psychotherapy. Another's life-long sinus problems have been dispelled by a change in diet. On television we see operations performed in China using acupuncture as an anaesthetic. In Chinese villages 'barefoot doctors' offer traditional Chinese herbal medicines. An Indian colleague tells how an ayurvedic treatment for a chronic skin condition works much better than anything she has had from a Western doctor. Through the women's movement we learn of herbs to relieve period pains and how to use yoghurt and vinegar to treat mild thrush. In the Community Health Council we get more and more requests from working-class people for help with finding alternative practitioners. As strong defenders of the NHS, we are perplexed by the dilemma of helping people go private. It is disturbing that so many people seem to have found help through services the NHS will not provide.

For some conditions both ordinary medicine (often referred to as allopathic medicine) and other forms of healing are at a loss. For conditions like cancer, claims of new breakthroughs are often made by both traditions, and how much truth there is in them always requires careful investigation. Many alternative practitioners do treat cancer, however – some alongside of, and some instead of, orthodox treatments. Very few would claim they had any answers, but some would say their forms of treatment are at least as effective as allopathic treatments, while being much less uncomfortable. For some conditions ordinary medicine without dispute offers the best course of action. There is no substitute for antibiotics in meningitis and other life-threatening infections. All other treatments work too slowly. For many chronic conditions, however, forms of healing to be found outside the NHS can offer far more than the doctor's surgery or the hospital outpatients clinic.

Of course not everyone gets better. Some spend a lot of time and money trailing from one practitioner to another with no success. The long-distance lorry driver has seen five different kinds of practitioners, but his back pain has not gone away. The teacher who has been getting migraine once a fortnight since her husband left her has had little relief from herbalists, naturopaths or acupuncturists. So much of healing is to do with changing our lives. And for most people this is so hard that there can be no magic answers.

Shan, Ruth and Vera all speak well of other forms of healing.

Shan describes affectionately the healing system she left behind in Guyana:

> When people get ill at home they look after one another more. When they are ill we use natural cures. If people get eczema there is a natural cure. The eczema could come from an ant bite, a mosquito bite, or overworking your hands in the rice field. They make a poultice of bush herbs and at least you get better with it. When you get a high temperature we boil up a special herb called fever grass and add it to the bath. It brings the fever up, so you sweat it out and then the fever cools.

Ruth also misses traditional Jamaican healing. Had she stayed in Jamaica her health problems might have been different, but she feels she might have had more help from her friends and family in dealing with her menstrual pain than she did in England.

Vera won't got to the doctor with her arthritis, although she has difficulty in getting around. She has heard that drugs are unlikely to be effective. Instead she has bought a book on treating arthritis with diet and has found that not eating any fruit or animal fats and giving up tea and coffee has eased it.

Vera and Ruth are also strong advocates of psychotherapy. Ruth says over and over again 'I know my need was not physical', and at one stage even asked, unsuccessfully, to be referred to the Tavistock Clinic. Vera sees a close connection between therapy and political action. She sees small mutual support groups – on the model of the women's movement – providing a place where you can explore problems and gain the strength to do something about them.

Vera and Ruth would have liked to consult alternative practitioners. What stopped them of course was money. Among alternative practitioners there is a spectrum of opinion about the rights and wrongs of charging patients, just as there is among allopathic doctors. Some, like the NHS consultants who also work in Harley Street, enjoy lucrative private practices and would not want it any other way. There is also a school of thought which says that patients are more committed to their treatment if they have paid for it. But many regret their exclusion from the NHS and would like not to be forced to charge. Some offer a sliding scale of charges according to income, but this is very much second-best. Healing skills should not have to be bought and sold in the market place, they argue.

Exclusion

The primary reason why alternative forms of healing are not available on the NHS is not that their practitioners did not want to be part of the service, but that the medical profession has fought a long battle to exclude them. Yet the energy and persistence with which medicine has contested other healing traditions is perhaps one reason for taking them more seriously. We tend to assume that historically paid physicians opposed the herbalists and lay healers because their methods were ineffective or dangerous. Yet there is considerable evidence that it was because these methods did work that they were threatened.

As long ago as 1322, when Jacoba Felicie was charged by the Faculty of Medicine at the University of Paris, the main accusation against her was that 'she would cure her patients of internal and external abscesses.' Later, English physicians sent a petition to parliament bewailing the 'worthless and presumptuous women who usurp the profession', demanding fines and imprisonment for women practising medicine. These women were not accused of ineffective or dangerous treatment, but of having dared to heal at all. And then there were the witches, whose crimes included providing contraceptive measures, performing abortions and offering drugs to ease the pain of labour. The church denounced non-professional healing as equivalent to heresy. 'If a woman dare cure without having studied, she is a witch and must die.' To be a witch it was not necessary to have been shown to have done harm. To heal was a crime in itself.

Women made up over 85 per cent of those who were executed. Estimates of the total number of deaths throughout Europe have been in millions.[11]

In later years non-medical healers were not burnt at the stake, but the pressure from medicine to restrict their activities continued. In the 1890s in Britain the medical profession consistently opposed the granting of a charter which would have given herbalists the status of registered practitioners. Physicians ridiculed the herbalists' 'quaint and absurd medicaments'. Among one list of the 'trivial medicines now obsolete among physicians' attacked by the medical profession were horehound, agrimony, elecampane, garlic, marsh-mallow, comfrey and colts-foot, all known today to have powerful healing qualities. From 1911, when Lloyd George's National Insurance Act was passed, it became virtually impossible for insured people to claim for attending the herbalist as they were now able to do for allopathic doctors. In 1934 parliament, under pressure from the BMA, threw out the Boothby Bill which would have legitimized osteopathy.

Even today, despite medicine's growing consciousness of the limitations of what it can do, particularly in the treatment of chronic conditions, it continues its closed and ungracious attitude to other approaches. In 1979 the Department of Health funded an investigation of Hakims, who practise traditional Unani medicine in Asian communities in Britain. In their report[12] the authors point out that practitioners in Pakistan and India undertake three- or four-year courses, and that the healing system, which involves changes in diet and the use of herbs, is often much more popular on the sub-continent than Western medicine. The recommendations of the report, however, focus on the possible dangers of some of the Hakim's metal-based medicines and the need to drive out 'abuse' by unqualified practitioners. As a result the Hakims and those who go to them were ridiculed in the specialist medical and nursing press. Article after article appeared – 'Your friendly neighbourhood Hakim',[13]

'Risk from Asian "healers"'[14] – written in a way which could only fuel racism and suspicion of traditional healing.

A sense that medicine has achieved its present domination less by the proven superiority of its methods than by the ruthless near-extermination of its rivals increases the urgency of re-exploring the oppressed traditions.

Our tradition

The tradition from which modern NHS medicine is descended has its roots in services to be paid for by those at the top of society who could afford paid physicians, while alternative medicine has its roots in healing relationships which did not involve payment. The paid physicians were normally men, while the lay healers were most often women. Paradoxically the healing attention we now pay for was once the people's medicine, with its roots in oral traditions going back to before the time of the witches. In contrast, what we now get free – with the important exception of prescription charges – is the descendant of rich people's medicine, developed through financial incentives rather than need. What is significant about this latter approach is not only that it was practised among the well-off, but that it was shaped by being a saleable commodity.

Some commentators[15] have argued that this division between healing skills developed without payment and medicine to be paid for has led to an essential difference between the two traditions. Alternative approaches usually work slowly. They are gentle and do not have the side effects of modern medicine. They are based on the philosophy that the body can – and usually does – get better by itself, but that this process can be encouraged. Hence the term 'healing'. Medicine prefers the bolder term 'cure'. Modern doctoring shares with its predecessors in the 'heroic' days of mustard plasters, purges, mercury and bleeding a prefer-ence for an instant impact, with quick and dramatic treatments.

Today's 'alternative medicine' is sometimes seen as a middle-class phenomenon. It is true that obviously more better-off people go to alternative practitioners because they can afford them. But there is also a sense in which non-allopathic forms of medicine can be seen as the proper heritage of the working class. Since the Industrial Revolution the form of medicine has been a live issue in both the American and the British working-class movements. The American Popular Health Movement, which was closely linked with emerging feminist and revolutionary politics in the early nineteenth century, advocated practices drawn from native American healing lore and advocated the withdrawal of medicine from the market place.[16] The Thompsonian system at the core of the American movement was brought to Britain by Dr Albert Coffin. 'Coffinism', whose practice was based on herbalism but which also attacked the adulteration of food, the hazards of the mills and the long hours of work, consciously directed itself to the working class in the northern industrial towns. Coffin told an audience in Sheffield in 1847:

> My object is to benefit the working class and I believe I have done them more good than could derive from the old practice of medicine. I believe the working classes are the only classes who deserve to have any good done to them.[17]

Even today, particularly in the North of England and among black people, there is working-class enthusiasm for herbalism and natural healing. In some parts every small town still has a herbalist. A middle-aged woman has chronic indigestion. The herbalist suggests one or two remedies. 'But the important thing', he says, 'is to work out if it is to do with what you are eating. Make a chart. Every day write down what you have to eat and how the pain is.' Her neighbour in the queue joins in: 'It is probably fatty foods; you should watch them particularly.' Despite the chaos and the crowds there is good humour. For a moment there is a sense that we are all equal partners in the difficult job of working out how to get better.

On the NHS

To say that the health service today should embrace other forms of healing is not to advocate them all uncritically. One of the problems that being outlawed by medicine has caused is a reluctance among alternative practitioners to get involved in evaluations of their work. They fear that people who do not understand their framework and assumptions will use any such research to discredit particular approaches in alternative medicine.

For similar reasons there is no tradition of developing practice by constantly publishing research, as there is in allopathic medicine. One of the advantages of legitimizing and putting resources into alternative practice would be to enable more evaluation and development to happen.

Another drawback of being outside the health service has been that there has been less interchange between different forms of healing practice than could be beneficial. When healing skills are to be paid for, some practitioners may feel they have an investment in secret knowledge, limiting what they are prepared to share either with each other or with patients. Some people say that they have found alternative practitioners just as authoritarian, or just as mystifying, as ordinary doctors. To say that alternative forms of healing should be part of the health service is not to say they are perfect. Developments in practice and changes of approach might emerge, however, once the process of interchange between differing traditions and with patients was made easier.

The terms under which alternative medicine might come within the framework of a health service would be complex. Some practitioners fear that orthodox medicine would try to absorb bits and pieces from other approaches while not overthrowing its allopathic framework. For instance, the value of acupuncture for pain relief is now being assessed in the NHS, following the discovery that it stimulates endorphins, biochemical agents in the brain with properties similar to opiates.

Alternative practitioners argue that by taking only those parts of acupuncture which can be seen to fit into the allopathic model, the holistic context which is crucial to its practice will be lost. To attempt a synthesis of orthodox and alternative approaches prematurely could be disastrous, particularly if orthodox medicine calls the tune. A plurality of approaches should be on offer. Alternative practitioners must be given guarantees that their healing traditions would not be interfered with. Bringing alternative practitioners into the health service would also make it much easier to work out what practitioner to go to. At the moment it is possible to waste a lot of money doing the rounds before finding a practitioner with skills appropriate to your particular problem. The health service could overcome this by providing experienced advisers to help patients to sort out options.

In trying to get the skills of herbalists, acupuncturists, naturopaths, osteopaths and psychotherapists available to all who want them, we are up against more than we may imagine. Obviously there will be opposition from the medical profession. The pharmaceutical industry won't like it, because a move towards other forms of healing could diminish the market for their products. Perhaps most importantly, those who hold ruling 'high-productivity' values both inside and outside the health service are unlikely to be enthusiastic. What the non-allopathic methods have in common is that proper healing often takes time (although there are quick methods for acute conditions). And time is something neither hospital managers nor workplace employers can give away. A quick antibiotic and you can be out of the hands of the NHS and back on the production line in no time.

Taking time is the characteristic which links the alternative practices. Not just time to get better, but time in consultation. For all that some alternative practitioners may mirror their orthodox colleagues in being patronizing or mystifying, they share a commitment to recognizing that helping a person to heal involves listening to them and trying to build up a picture of that person's world. Because most alternative practitioners do not have a class perspective, they are sometimes reluctant to recognize all the things that prevent us from changing our lives. They may not have a perspective of helping us to identify the *common* origins of our ill health, but their emphasis on *biography* as well as physical examination is surely an essential step to the kind of medicine we need.

A NEW MEDICINE

These changes – a new emphasis on care, an openness to alternative medicine, and a commitment to oppose the social forces which damage our health – are essential first steps in developing a more appropriate health care. But what we want is more than changes in attitudes and priorities. In as much as our critique of health care goes beyond the problems of organization and ideology to the categories and concepts at the heart of medicine, as we discussed in Chapter 8, it is at this level, too, that medicine must change.

Conceiving of a new medicine lies beyond the limits of present imagination. But it is possible to see how the changes we have described might begin to form the basis for a new practice. What we need is a medicine which is conscious of the way in which present practice reproduces ruling ideas, cutting us off both from an understanding of the nature of health and illness and from possibilities for healing, and begins to challenge these.

The most urgent task is to look again at concepts of causality. We need a medicine which seeks explanations of what happens to people's bodies not only at the level of germs and pathology but also in terms of people's social world. With this change of emphasis, we need new ways of thinking about the processes by which our social world can affect our bodies. This requires abandoning the old-fashioned mechanistic view of the way in which heads and bodies interact, replacing it with a recognition that people's emotional lives and feelings can bear directly on their bodies. We need to abandon the notion that it is unusual or extraordinary to find our life experience affecting our health, and replace it with a recognition that our social world has an everyday impact on our bodies.

The social world is often seen as affecting our heads, our psychology, while the physical world – the world of pollution and germs – affects our bodies. But this way of seeing human beings in two bits precludes all kinds of other possibilities. Feelings and experiences are not simply a cerebral matter; they do not just affect our minds. They affect our bodies all the time. Deep in our culture there is a recognition of this. We know exactly what people mean when they say 'I had butterflies in my stomach' or 'It sent shivers down my spine.' But these notions do not fit in with dominant ways of looking at health. A new medicine would develop a language for talking about the impact of feelings on bodies, for describing the realm of experience which is neither entirely psychological nor physical. This would not mean imposing ideas, but legitimizing and building on the language which already exists in our culture.[18]

With new ideas about what causes illness would come a new framework for diagnosis and a new naming system for illness. What this might be is hard to envisage. It might abandon the present notion that to name an illness is to imply knowledge of its physiological cause. It could draw on the quite different frameworks for diagnosing and naming conditions within alternative medicine. It might involve far more precise differentiation of symptoms and a reordering of them into different systems of classification.

Another central focus for a new medicine would be on a different approach to finding out what is wrong. Listening to what people have to say about their lives would be as important as examining their bodies. This emphasis on biography, on understanding people's health in terms of their physical and social environment, is already the practice in many alternative approaches to healing. One difficulty with these forms of healing at present is that they sometimes overestimate the possibilities for people to change their lives individually, seeing this as a matter of personal rather than collective responsibility. What is needed is a medicine which expands the holistic approach of alternative medicine into a recognition of the political nature of the person's social and physical environment – and follows this with a search for forms of *collective* action which may alleviate or remedy the problem.

To speak of the need for listening and for collective action is not to underestimate the difficulties of finding out what may be causing a problem or the fact that problems with collective origins almost always manifest themselves in very personal or individual ways. Often you cannot find out what is wrong simply by listening, and the strongest collective action in the world may not be able to put it right. We tend to think of psychotherapy as primarily to do with mental health problems (where it should be far more extensively available); but techniques from therapy and counselling can also be invaluable in helping to reveal the causes of health problems. Sadly, just as there is a divide between alternative and allopathic medicine, there has not been a strong tradition of interaction between the psychotherapy movement and the alternative healing movement, although there are signs that this is changing. A new practice could fruitfully draw on all traditions.

It is sometimes said that psychotherapy is an unacceptable approach to dealing with problems that have social roots and should be the subject of political action. Yet there is no more logic in this view than in saying that people with physical illnesses should not seek help with them because they have social causes. In both cases we seek help to find the strength and energy to confront what is damaging us. We need therapy which helps us explore the roots of our pain and suffering and gives us the strength and confidence to struggle to change our lives.

This is how one woman involved in therapy put it:

The problem about the idea of therapy is that it seems as if it is about sick people 'getting better'. I am not sick. Deep down I am a healthy person trying to find my power – the power I need to live my life to the full and confront this sick society. Therapy helps me do this.[19]

Therapy can be empowering, and this should also be true of medicine as a whole. Just as medicine can learn from politics about what is making us ill, so in our political action we need to learn from healing practice.

Vera puts it this way:

Woe betide you if you have got anywhere in your notes that you are neurotic. Then every single pain is due to neurosis. In fact that has got the core of truth. Approached in a different way, in a non-blaming way, the core could be explored. I do believe that most of the things I suffer are caused by my way of living. By what I live in and what I live amongst. That is why I am such a believer in support groups and talking. Us getting together and helping each other is terribly important. It is the confidence you get, the power that you get back a bit. That is what should happen with a group of people meeting together.

Medicine cannot solve our health problems. It cannot magic away the social forces which bear upon our health. But it could help us to feel a bit less powerless. The medicine we need would recognize both that there are possibilities for healing open to us now and that there are many health problems without immediate solutions. It would acknowledge that, however clearly our problems arise from common conditions of life, our suffering is unique and personal. It would seek to alleviate that suffering without losing sight of the social forces which give rise to it. It would see our problems as rooted not just in a hazardous and impoverished environment but in the *social* relations of late capitalism. Its job would be to generate some ammunition and help us to find some strength with which to resist.

The changes we need will come from the bottom of the health service, not the top. New kinds of practice are conceived and fought for on the ground. They cannot be willed into being overnight by right-thinking policy-makers. Fundamental changes in the structure and organization of the health service, however, are essential to create the conditions in which appropriate health care can develop.

Defending free health care

What is great about the NHS and very special is that it is free at the time of use. Before the NHS was set up, and still today in many countries, illness was compounded by worries about how to pay for treatment. Equally important, when health care is to be paid for, services relate less to people's needs than to where there is money to be made. Thirty years on, the shape of health care still bears the stamp of market medicine, but at least the need to obtain a financial return for health care services no longer presents an obstacle to change. Unless health care is kept outside the market, there is no possibility of developing services appropriate to our needs.

Today the hard-won principle of socialized health care is being nibbled away. Rocketing prescription charges, dental and optical charges are now deterring many people from using the service. Government encouragement to private health insurance schemes and private hospitals, combined with the impoverishment of the NHS, provide both carrot and stick to create conditions in which the private sector can flourish. We are right to feel edgy that the whole basis of the NHS is threatened. Abolishing charges, curbing the private sector and defending a free health service are the preconditions of any further positive changes.

Democracy

The present decision-making structure in the health service has to go. The system of appointing rather than electing those who sit on district and regional health authorities and the present medical domination of these bodies is entirely inappropriate. But what do we mean when we say the system should be more democratic?

Is it sufficient to change the structure of formal decision-making in the district or regional health authorities? Can we envisage control by workers and users at all levels of decision-making? Should decisions about the organization of work be made by meetings of workers in each ward and clinic? How should the need for democracy be balanced against the need for quick, efficient decisions? Should workers send representatives to district level meetings? Would the unions be involved or stay separate, keeping their traditional distance from what could be seen as management? Would the doctors still dominate? How could the informal power which comes with their class and historic status be counteracted?

And how would the interests of the people who use the service be represented? Long-stay hospitals can have a patients' committee. These hospitals are people's homes, and they should determine what happens in them. But the interest of potential users is wider than the people who happen to be ill at any one time. Should delegates from unions outside the health service, patients' committee or community groups represent the patients' interest on decision-making bodies? Already about thirty general practices have patients' committees.[1] Should this movement be encouraged?

There is no reason why every part of the country should have the same decision-making structure. In different places different forms of organization could be tried out. How the new forms of organization turned out would depend a lot on how we had organized our struggle in the first place. New forms of democratic decision-making will emerge from the ways of organizing we have in opposition.

Redistributing knowledge

Taking real, rather than formal, control over health care means doing more than democratizing today's health care institutions. We need a redistribution of knowledge about caring, healing and the nature of health and illness which breaks down the present divide between health workers and the rest of us. This is not a recent view. Barbara Ehrenreich and Deirdre English argue that it is only in the last century that the tradition of lay healing has been undermined successfully by medicine:

All but the most privileged women were expected to be at least literate in the language of herbs and healing techniques; the most learned women travelled widely to share their skills ... The rise of the experts was not the inevitable triumph of right over wrong, fact over myth, it began as a bitter conflict which set women against men, class against class. Women did not learn to look to external 'science' until after their old skills had been ripped away.[2]

In this century there have been many attempts to re-establish a tradition in which knowledge about health is not the sole prerogative of full-time health workers. The Chinese barefoot doctors were originally elected by neighbours or workmates to be the first point of contact when you felt ill or needed advice about health, but they continued with their daily work. Carlos Biro, a Mexican doctor who developed a four-month training programme in basic medical skills, argues that 85 per cent of people's health problems involve a limited number of complaints. What is essential is that in basic training barefoot or lightly shod doctors should learn to judge what *they cannot cope with* and must be referred to health workers with more experience and skill.[3]

What we want in industrialized countries today is not to have the burden of healing and caring returned to us without support from the health service, but to have sufficient knowledge to have the confidence to deal with minor illness, to meet NHS full-timers on more equal terms and to be able to challenge what is making us ill. Even today there are non-health workers who advise their families, neighbours and colleagues on health questions, among them older people who remember their grandparents' healing remedies, lay healers within black communities, women who have been active in the women's health movement, and some shop stewards and safety reps. These activities should be supported and developed with a far wider dissemination of knowledge.

The view that it is a precondition of our liberation that we refuse to surrender our autonomy to the experts was expounded over a hundred years ago in the most vehement terms by Herbert Shelton, an activist in the nineteenth-century American Popular Health Movement:

> Any system that, of itself, creates a privileged class who can by law or otherwise, lord it over their fellow men destroys true freedom and personal autonomy. Any system that teaches the sick that they can get well only through the exercise of the skill of someone else, and that they remain alive only through the tender mercies of the privileged class, has no place in nature's scheme of things and the sooner it is abolished, the better mankind will be.[4]

Division of labour

How should health care be done? Is there any reason why health work should be divided between doctors, nurses, paramedical staff and ancillary workers, as it is at the moment? Is the rigid division between medicine and nursing, curers and carers, historically male and female, what we want? Could the tasks involved in health care be shared out in a different way? There will always need to be people with special skills and expertise, but maybe all health workers could begin by doing general caring work, assisting in the whole range of health service activities, and then begin to specialize as they found out what they enjoyed doing and could do best. And maybe those specialisms could take a different form than at present. We can try to imagine what the nurse/doctor might be like. Already there are some nurse practitioners who carry out medical intervention on their own without instructions from doctors. There might also be ways in which people doing ancillary jobs could move on to learn other skills.

We also need to consider how the non-allopathic practitioners could be involved. Would they be funded by the health service, but still practice in separate premises entirely away from the old allopathic centres? Or would they take part in the daily life of clinics and hospitals interchanging their skills? Could a new kind of health worker emerge equipped with skills from nursing, non-allopathic healing and medicine? Today's alternative practitioners do have a limited involvement in the NHS. Some GPs have homeopathic training, and consultants have been known to refer their patients regularly to osteopaths. But at the moment these arrangements are very much on orthodox medicine's terms. New ways would need to be found of ensuring the equal participation of the two traditions.

Medicine in its place

Medical authority will be reduced only when it is faced with a stronger challenge from unions, individual health workers and patients. But institutional changes, such as democracy, would help. And changes in training could be important too.

Often it is said that the problem with medicine is that there is too much high technology and not enough primary care. An anti-technology stand can blind us to the value of some forms of medical intervention. The problem is not that all high-technology medicine and the use of drugs are a bad thing, but that because there is money to be made by the pharmaceutical and medical technology companies, because it is satisfying for doctors to try out new equipment, and because it is hard to say no to anything that may be potentially life-saving, the therapeutic value of many forms of medical intervention never gets properly assessed.

What is needed is not rigid positions, but a far more careful evaluation and assessment of unproven medical technologies, from intensive care baby units to whole body scanners. Already there are steps in this direction. Clinical trials do take place and in some hospitals there are rigorous 'medical audits' in which doctors look at cases that went wrong and subject themselves to mutual criticism. The problem is that these assessments are done by doctors and may take place within a framework of medical values. We need processes which open up the evaluation of medical intervention to other health workers and lay people and enable a far wider discussion of the methods and criteria to be used in that evaluation. Some of the issues would be complex. How to assess the quality of life engendered by particular treatments is one thorny area. Another difficult issue is how to decide priorities when resources are limited, as they almost inevitably always will be, however much is spent on health care. At the moment more is spent on sophisticated medicine than routine care because prestige medicine has the power to attract resources. With new decision-making structures the present informal mechanisms for deciding priorities would be replaced by other less hidden processes. It would be a mistake, however, to believe that this will make it easier to determine the relative priority of kidney machines or home nurses, for instance.

Education

Centres of specialist expertise would not be redundant, but health workers should not receive their basic education in these elite places removed from where people live. With or without a different division of labour, between nurses, doctors, paramedical and ancillary staff, training must change. Gail Young, a senior house officer in a northern hospital, described the changes she would like to see:

> Big changes are needed in undergraduate training. Attempts are already being made at some medical schools to provide courses which give early emphasis to patient contact, community medicine, and try to integrate the study of the sciences with patient care. Perhaps medical students should work as nursing auxiliaries for a while. Greater emphasis should be placed on teaching methods of finding and using information rather than the present cramming with superfluous factual detail. Emphasis should always be laid on thinking of patients as whole people and relating their own experiences to one's own experience and life. Creativity should be encouraged rather than crushed beneath tomes of dry facts. Time should be found to discuss feeling about patients and reactions to work. Competitiveness should be discouraged and free discussion involving nursing and paramedical staff encouraged. Students should learn to deal with patients' relatives in a sensitive way.[5]

Carlos Biro, who trained the Mexican *huarache* doctors, taught his students in a neighbourhood clinic, arguing that unfeeling scientific researchers and superspecialists are bred by a curriculum which begins by introducing students to dead bodies and goes on to allow them to meet live ones in a setting entirely divorced from the rest of their lives. As well as receiving training in basic medicine, minor surgery, medical psychology and diet, his students spent time taking part in the activities of the clinic and in visiting people in their homes. Throughout the course, emphasis was given to psychosocial aspects of health and time spent helping students to work through their own distress arising from what they had learned from ill people.

Research

A major shift in research priorities is required. More effort is needed in the evaluation of existing procedures and technology. A whole new area could develop assessing the relevance of different allopathic and non-allopathic approaches. For years research on alternative medicine has been hampered by lack of money and official interest. Far more effort could usefully be directed into it. More research could profitably be done on what is making us ill. A far higher proportion of research effort should go into epidemiology. At present, however, epidemiological methods are primarily used to link specific pathogens with specific illnesses. New methodologies would be needed to explore the relationship between illness and forms of social organization. An epidemiology intended to promote change in society as a whole rather than make small-scale adjustments to the environment would need to develop new approaches. We need more effort put into studying why people at the top of society are well, rather than yet more investigations of the people at the bottom.[6] We need an epidemiology which is appropriate to the lives of women as well as men, and explores gender differences as thoroughly as class differences. The new methods might make less use of statistics and more of people's life experience. We could see the growth of what might be called *collated biography*, piecing together people's individual histories and looking for common patterns in the experience of people with similar conditions. There could also be far more care-oriented research, developing the technologies of disabled living and of pain relief.

At the moment most research in Britain is either carried out by the drug companies or funded by rival industries. The tobacco industry funds research on occupational health. Research on cyclamates, a rival sweetener to sugar, was funded by the sugar industry. Research for a vaccine against tooth decay has been funded by a sweet manufacturer. Research on the dangers of butter is funded by margarine companies. Research on the dangers of margarine is funded by the butter companies. And most research on the hazards of drugs and toxic chemicals is carried out by the manufacturers themselves. New procedures are needed for deciding the direction of research, and new methods of funding it will have to be found.

Research should be accountable to the people being researched. Resources should be available to women's groups, community groups and unions to commission research or obtain advice and help with carrying out their own research. Local health research is already happening. In Leeds bus workers carried out their own survey of the effects of the stress of the job;[7] and many other safety reps have done their own surveys too. In Oldham a tenants' group did its own research on dampness and illness,[8] and other tenants' associations have also investigated the impact of their housing conditions on their collective health.

In general, research effort needs to be diversified, with more emphasis on causes and less on cures. In practice, how much the enormous levels of effort and energy now going into the search for biochemical and microbiological answers might be attenuated would be a matter for long debate and discussion. It will be no easy task to moderate the powerful influence of the pharmaceutical and medical technology companies in determining what research is done.

The pharmaceutical companies

At present the problem with the drug companies is not just that they rip off the NHS, making huge profits out of public funds. Their activities also profoundly influence the way health care develops. Taking the drug companies out of private ownership is an essential first step, but formally nationalizing them might not be sufficient to undermine their grip on health care. It would also be necessary to have new procedures for deciding what drugs should be developed and what abandoned, for working out directions for research, for controlling their safety and efficacy and for monitoring side effects.[9]

Once drug production was not organized for profit, there would be no pressure on doctors to use previously heavily promoted products. Changes in prescribing patterns would also reduce demand. There is plenty of evidence that we could get by with fewer drugs. In 1971 the US Food and Drug administration investigated 2,000 marketed drugs and found that 60 per cent lacked evidence for their therapeutic claims.[10] Experience in Third World countries has shown that basic needs could be covered by 1 or 2 per cent of marketed drugs. An Indian government committee, for instance, has established that, of the 15,000 drugs on sale in India, only 118 are essential.[11] On the basis of our present expectations, a larger number of medicines might be judged to be essential in Britain, but it could well be far fewer than the number currently purchased by the NHS.

While in general the overall contribution of medicines to therapy should be reduced, there is a case for developing the more widespread use of herbal and homeopathic medicines. There is now even a growing interest in the traditional medicines from the multinational drug companies, who want to capture and market their secrets. Meanwhile the World Health Organization has its own project to collect and distribute information about the use of non-allopathic medicines throughout the world. Non-allopathic medicines cannot be substituted for pharmaceutical products, because they are used in a different way, in conjunction with diet, for instance. Nevertheless some resources previously used in the production and consumption of the products of the drug companies could be used in making non-allopathic medicines more widely available.

Record keeping

We should have the right to see our medical records and hospital notes. Our lack of this right is an important factor in our unequal power with doctors. We should be able to know what our diagnosis is, what the treatment is, and what comments have been made to be passed on to whoever else reads the record.

It is also essential that there should be strict safeguards on who else can have access to records. Recent attempts by the police to obtain the right to look at doctors' files, and computerization, which potentially opens up access to other authorities, such as employers or social security officials, make safeguards on records a live issue.

Medical records can have a very positive function too. If they contain the right kind of data, they can provide vital epidemiological information, highlighting higher rates of illness among people doing a particular job or living in a particular neighbourhood. Computer technology opens up the possibility of using this kind of method for identifying hazards far more widely. Medical record systems need to be designed so that information needed for this kind of analysis can be stored and retrieved, while guaranteeing personal anonymity.

Organization

The more often you are likely to need a service, the nearer it should be to your home. What is needed are neighbourhood centres offering all the kinds of health care we need regularly, including access to non-allopathic practitioners. In the neighbourhood centre you should also be able to find your compulsive eating group or the support group for people with epilepsy. The centre should deal with minor casualties too. When seeing specialists does not require complicated diagnostic tests, this could be done here. It is far easier for one specialist to get into his or her car and spend a morning at the centre than for half a dozen sick people to stagger to the hospital on the bus. All the facilities needed for home care should be based in the neighbourhood. In the same centre you should be able to ask for a home nurse or a wheelchair or some more batteries for your hearing aid.

The idea of health centres has a long history. In the 1930s the Peckham health centre was established with the aim of health promotion for the whole family. Medical services were provided alongside recreational facilities, including a swimming pool. The intention was to strengthen people in this working-class neighbourhood to resist disease. Although the founders of the Peckham health centre were not socialists, the centre became a model for members of the Socialist Medical Association, who argued before the setting up of the NHS that primary care should be about helping people keep healthy as well as dealing with them when they are sick.

A small proportion of British GPs now work from health centres. But most are a far cry from the ideals of Peckham and other experimental projects run by socialist health workers in the same period. Today's health centres are still very much doctor-dominated and do little more in the field of health promotion than GPs, school nurses, health visitors and home nurses working individually. Nevertheless there are models to draw on. A handful of group practices within the NHS have developed a very different and far more oppositional style. Health centres in Cuba are organized with a small team of health workers for each block of streets. Each centre has an epidemiologist as well as doctors, dentists, nurses and therapists and a worker whose job it is to advise local people on environmental health. In the USA and Australia feminist health centres have been established, helping women to learn about their bodies and take control of their own health as well as providing advice and treatment.

Where care cannot happen in people's homes, a lot more of it should happen near them. People's lives should be able to go on as near as possible as before their illness. Every neighbourhood should contain small units for the frail elderly, the mentally handicapped and the mentally ill, and for people with illnesses such as bronchitis which need care without sophisticated medical intervention.

Beyond the neighbourhood there is always the hospital. It will take out appendices and mend broken bones as ever. For rare conditions and treatment with sophisticated technology, people should expect to travel further. One way of controlling the proliferation of expensive technology is to limit the places where it can be used, while giving grants to sick people and their visitors to cover the cost of travel. It is a relatively small price to be paid for shifting the balance of resource provision into the direction of everyday care.

It may be helpful to think of health care happening at three levels: in the neighbourhood, in the general hospital and in specialist centres. Today it is in the specialist centres that the excitement of medicine is to be found. The rest is regarded as rather mundane and carries low status. Can we envisage a scenario with the excitement at the neighbourhood level, so that it is here that new understandings are achieved, new practices developed and new theories generated? Far away from the laboratories and operating theatres of the teaching hospital, here, in our neighbourhoods, a new medicine can be conceived and born.

14   Wishful Thinking

After the long quiescence of the early 1980s, a new period of social ferment has begun. Unions in the coal, steel, power and water industries have put in a joint pay claim with health workers, teachers and council workers. In recent years the practice of twinning the struggles of low-paid public sector workers with those of better-paid groups with greater industrial muscle, which first developed when miners stood on hospital picket lines and print workers stopped the presses of Fleet Street during the 1982 health workers' strike, has been seen more frequently. A summer of co-ordinated industrial action throughout the public sector is expected.

Within the unions a cultural revolution is taking place. The old paternalistic 'Leave it to me and I'll sort it out with the management' steward system is being overthrown. Many groups of workers, particularly women, black and young people, are challenging traditional labour movement definitions of their problems and the answers to them. They are demanding time for discussion of people's feelings and needs and developing new forms of collective action. The old slogan 'Together we are strong' has come alive. In these days of harsh penalties for trade union activity, when it is dangerous for anyone to be identified as an agitator, a new emphasis on doing it together is spreading throughout the workers' movement. In the new high-technology factories there have been a series of walk-outs, sit-ins and demonstrations following a crack-down on rocketing sickness absence rates. In the government workshops where the otherwise unemployed spend their days, exasperation at the meaningless 'work' and a sense that the pay is so low that there is nothing to lose have prompted widespread non-co-operation.

As council housing falls into greater disrepair, tenants whose rent is not paid directly from the DHSS to the council have taken to withholding it. In Glasgow, Leeds, Coventry and Newcastle there are now city-wide rent strikes. The money which would otherwise have gone in rent is being put into a special fund, and the tenants' associations are now organizing repairs for the households in greatest need paid for from the fund. The mounting tension with the authorities has brought a new sense of community. There is more neighbourliness. Older people keep an eye on the kids. Ill and disabled people find that someone pops in in the course of the day with some shopping and the latest news. Some young people have taken the lifts apart and found out how to mend them when they break down.

Now most of the left Labour councils, faced by the growing contradiction between their position as elected representatives of the people and their managerial responsibilities for a low-paid workforce and inadequate services, have resigned. But the legacy of their initiatives still remains. The health centre is one of these. Despite threats of closure from the new council, it has now been going for nearly five years.

From the outside the building is uninspiring. The once bright blue paintwork has now faded and fails to relieve the sobriety of the disused Victorian primary school. Over the door a greying sheet declares 'Occupied by workers and users: hands off!' On the wall above the high pointed windows 'Health for the people' has been recently painted on the brickwork in letters four feet high.

But inside there is a lot going on. The old children's cloakroom is cluttered with prams and pushchairs. Next to it is a crèche and beyond that an assortment of meeting and therapy rooms. On the left there is a large reception room. There are easy chairs and coffee tables in groups scattered around the room. On the wall a giant blackboard lists the afternoon's events and the rooms they are happening in. Last-minute alterations and additions give it a slightly chaotic look: Pain clinic, 2 p.m.; Antenatal group, 2 p.m.; Shiftwork research group, 3 p.m.; 'Basics of physiology and anatomy' course, 3 p.m.; Pensioners' health group, 1.30 p.m.; Massage workshop (NB. women only), 5 p.m.; Self-help therapy, 5 p.m.; Digestive problems pamphlet group, 4 p.m.; Mental patients' union, 3 p.m.; Lead action group, 6 p.m.; Bad backs anonymous, 5.30 p.m.; Tobacco action group, 7 p.m.; Psoriasis self-help, 5 p.m.; Introduction to work hazards class, 6 p.m. Under the 'New events' heading a workshop for women on 'training for confrontation with the police' next Saturday is announced. A new discussion group is starting; its first session will be on 'Bronchial problems among women and children: oppression or housing?' It is hoped to start a counselling service for gay and heterosexual couples in the near future. Along the bottom of the blackboard it says 'Remember: to see the practitioners you will need an appointment. If it is an emergency tell the receptionists.'

The receptionists are the health centre's most highly experienced workers. They have all trained in at least one form of healing and have been through a year of intensive study, sharing their knowledge accumulated through their differing training and experience. Elizabeth was trained as a naturopath, John as a nurse, Mary and David as NHS doctors, Sheila as a dentist; Doreen was a shop steward specializing in health and safety; Sita was a counsellor in a rape crisis centre; Maria was a tenants' activist and Daren was a physiotherapist. Although they come from different backgrounds, they share the view that each tradition of healing and action offers a partial view of what to do about illness. They try to develop their skills through learning from, and arguing with, each other. Their job is to meet everyone who brings a health problem to the centre and talk over what might be done.

The centre has changed since it was founded by a handful of

non-allopathic practitioners and a couple of NHS doctors. In the early days there were no specialists to advise on possible courses of action. There were a few self-help groups, but these were seen as a sideline. The main emphasis was on one-to-one encounters. The change has come from people who use the centre and from discussions between the practitioners, stimulated by meeting groups running other centres up and down the country. The patients have continued to insist that the practitioners share their knowledge and skills. Now critical interchanges between workers and patients, which would have been unthinkable, are commonplace, reflecting the general mood of questioning in the wider society and the confidence built up through the centre's collective activities. The idea of receptionists and the greater emphasis on collective activities are two of the main changes.

Sometimes the receptionists simply offer advice. At other times they refer people either to one of the clinics, groups or classes running at the centre or to see one of the centre's practitioners individually. The practitioners have backgrounds either in orthodox or in alternative medicine, including naturopathy, homeopathy, massage, acupuncture and physiotherapy, and there is a dentist too. A man in his mid-forties with chronic back pain is encouraged to join the 'Bad backs anonymous' group. This group meets twice a week with a physiotherapist trained in yoga who has developed a series of exercises to relieve back pain. In the group men and women talk about why they think the pain first came, when it is worst and so on. Sometimes through these discussions the physiotherapist recommends seeing one of the other practitioners, often the work safety adviser or the psychotherapist.

A toddler has a persistent cough. The father thinks antibiotics might be the answer. The receptionist advises that these are unlikely to be helpful, as it is a long-term problem. She suggests inhaling steam and some changes in diet. The receptionist asks the father why he thinks the child is ill. He mentions the damp, which the council insists is condensation. It is a big problem for all the families in his block. The receptionist remembers other cases she has seen from the same area and suggests the man meets the tenants' liaison worker, who will discuss it with the tenants' association.

Sometimes it is hard for the receptionist to work out what the problem is or the best course of action. Sometimes a person can come back to see the receptionist three or four times before a referral is made. A woman has recurrent fevers and painful glands. She sleeps a lot, has very little energy and is on the verge of despair. Earlier the receptionist had suggested seeing one of the orthodox doctors, who had sent her to the hospital for tests. The hospital had found nothing definite other than that she had a virus infection. The receptionist suggests she sees the centre's naturopath, who has taken a special interest in this kind of illness.

An elderly man complains of rheumatism. The receptionist explains that no one really understands much about it. The herbalist or the naturopath might help. There are lots of people waiting, but the man is not satisfied. The receptionist is torn; she does not have the time the man needs. A continual discussion among the centre's workers and users is about how to balance the demands of all the people who come to the centre. The receptionist suggests the man joins the pensioners' health group. He is reluctant. 'I'm an individualist', he says. 'I don't like being herded together with a load of old fogies.'

A man in his fifties is deeply distressed. His face is tortured, and he complains of pains inside. He is vague about where it hurts and the nature of the pains. He appears seriously anxious. The practitioner, who trained in orthodox medicine, suspects that the problem is what used to be called 'psychosomatic', but he has also had rows with other centre workers and patients, who say he dismisses problems as 'just psychological' too easily. Whatever the problem the man will need a lot of time overcoming his fear. The receptionist suggests he sees a counsellor. The counsellor can perhaps discover more about the man's problem and then refer him either to the hospital for investigation or for therapy.

The centre's workers try to keep in mind the question 'Why is this person ill?' They ask people what they think their illnesses are about. They aim to build up a picture of what is wrong, by helping people to study their own lives and by using techniques from counselling and therapy. They know that many difficulties have their answers outside the realm of health care altogether, in relationships between people and the struggle for a better life. They see their job as exploring what is getting people down and helping them to find the strength to fight back. One of their catch-phrases is 'Build resistance!', summing up their medical and political aims.

Sometimes the 'what is to be done' that they work out is a prescription, some herbs or a change in diet. Sometimes it is joining a group, exploring problems together, learning from one another and the practitioner. At other times there are no immediate solutions or ways forward. So often illnesses arise from collective problems, which have only collective solutions. The health workers see their job as piecing together a better understanding of the causes of illness, as well as helping individuals.

People can choose which receptionist to see. If they want to see a particular person they have to come at a set time, because as the centre also opens in the evenings, the receptionists work shifts. Normally people talk to the receptionists in the reception area, but they can be seen in private if they wish.

Medical records are handed to people as they come in. The centre uses the records for epidemiological analysis and to help in the monitoring and evaluation of various approaches. Basic information is computerized, but there has been a lot of argument in the centre's co-ordinating committee about it. The epidemiologist says the system could yield vital information about pollution from local factories and work hazards. Its opponents say that any computerized record system in this day and age is dangerous. The hospital is already pressurizing the clinic to link its computer with theirs and this would mean giving the health authority, and anyone the health authority was acting for, direct information about the centre's users.

The issue of record keeping is one of the most controversial among both patients and workers. At first records were not given to people unless they asked to see them. Many users of the centre objected: 'You want to share knowledge, but you are still keeping it in your own hands.' One day a group came into the centre, asked for their records and then took them home, saying they would not bring them back until the system was changed. The centre's workers resisted. One comment was typical: 'Too much of what we say in the records is upsetting. I put "query brain cancer", just to remind myself every time someone comes in with a persistent headache. Do people really want to know that? And what about psychiatric diagnoses? Who wants to know they are a psychopath?' The health workers were shocked to be told 'If you think someone's a psychopath, the least you can do is tell them they are getting that label. As for brain cancer, isn't the point to change attitudes about diagnostic processes and cancer so they become less frightening?'

After more argument and heart-searching the record system was changed. But now a new issue has come up. It has come to light that the health workers keep a secret book in which they write extra things about people to warn each other if patients have a long history of violence, or if they have a pattern of abusing the centre's services or staff. The workers are now being accused of 'sham information sharing', and another row looms.

The centre serves a densely populated district in the north-western part of the city. Within the centre teams of workers take responsibility for each block or group of streets. Each team has a part-time administrator and an office, usually in someone's house in the block. The teams are accountable to the local residents' group, tenants' association or a specially elected committee where the block does not already have its own organization. The team, which includes a receptionist, a practitioner and two home care workers, as well as an administrator, sees its job as to be in touch with and aware of the health needs of the people in the block. They are concerned both with individuals – Mabel Wright is disabled and needs visiting every week; John Evans has severe bronchitis and would benefit from a home visit by a practitioner; Eileen Jones has just been discharged from hospital and needs someone to look after her kids – and with collective needs. One team is supporting a campaign against damp, for a children's garden and to close the road to traffic. It has also helped to set up a parents' and toddlers' group and a pensioners' lounge.

Each team operates in its own way. Some have a system of three-monthly check-ups for children, the elderly and the chronically sick, and have done house-to-house surveys on people's needs. Other teams reject this approach. For them it is reminiscent of the 'health surveillance' and 'at risk' registers in vogue in the 1970s. They argue that, in this era of social security snoopers and 'community' policing, anything that seems like prying is out. The systematic teams believe this means that some people are overlooked. The others rely on informal networks to find out people's needs. Health screening has also come under attack in some neighbourhoods. The health workers are trying to 'medicalize everyday life', taking over people's lives rather than helping them get on with them, it is said. The home care workers also run a mobile 'home care library', where you can borrow a commode, a wheelchair or a walking frame and get new supplies of incontinence pads or hearing aid batteries.

The minor casualty clinic occupies the other main room on the ground floor of the centre. It caters for 'walking wounded': children with dog bites, athletes with sprains, people with burns and cuts. Of all the services the clinic provides this one has been most bitterly opposed by the local health authority, who have accused the centre of 'barefootism': 'how will people know their injury is minor? Lives may be lost by not having access to appropriate technology.' In practice any case about which there is doubt is transferred to the hospital. Posters in the clinic, factories and the neighbourhood explain how to decide whether to go to the clinic or the hospital.

Down the corridor from the casualty clinic, the pain clinic is meeting. Of its six members, five suffer chronic pain, two through arthritis and three through car accidents. They have been brought to the clinic by the centre's ambulance. The sixth member of the group is an NHS-trained doctor who has taken special interest in the management of severe pain. The two hours begin with a patient leading a relaxation session. The group has been together eighteen months, and the members have come to know each other well. Together they have developed new methods of pain control using relaxation, breathing and visualization techniques. A couple of them have already started running similar groups at other health centres. Later in the session they talk about how they have been in the week. They find this sharing of experience beneficial. A middle-aged woman tells the group of a recent visit to hospital. She has been offered a device which uses electrical stimulation to abate pain. They discuss the ins and outs and encourage her to try it. Another man is upset; the drugs he is on are making him dozy. The hospital have no time for his complaints. It is agreed that one of the group will go with him to his next hospital appointment to get it discussed. Some of the group have been seeing the acupuncturist with some success and encourage the others to try it.

In an upstairs room the antenatal clinic is just finishing. Two midwives run the sessions. As well as doing a check-up they teach the women about what is happening to their bodies. Natural childbirth training is offered. In the groups there is discussion of the pros and cons of hospital and home delivery. The centre had hoped to set up its own maternity unit, but since the closure threat plans for expansion have been shelved. The women spend a lot of time just chatting, supporting each other in struggles with doctors and husbands. Where a woman is anxious or has had a bad experience, another offers to go with her to her next appointment. When the children are born, they will be able to bring them to the children's clinic here. Again there will be check-ups and time to discuss illnesses and worries, but there is also a lot of time spent talking about the women's own health, their kids' illnesses, about when to tell them off and whether to hit them, about feeding and sleeping and sex and social security.

The health centre workers use the term 'oppositional medicine'. They want to enable people to explore common problems affecting their health and support each other in daily struggles. These are sometimes very private conflicts, within families or with the housing department. It is part of their philosophy of healing that to identify a problem and get support in doing something about it is good for you. They see their women's therapy groups, mutual support groups and clinic sessions as an alternative to Valium and other pain-stoppers. They base their approach on what the women's movement calls 'consciousness raising'. The health workers talk of 'turning the pain outwards'. The theory is that instead of bearing the hurt of capitalist and patriarchal social relations inside yourself, you try to put it out and challenge it in the world.

But the health workers are also aware that the daily struggle is happening at work, on the estates and on the streets. All around as the momentum of the strike wave, the rent strikes, occupations and demonstrations grow, there seems to be boundless energy to confront the health-destructive conditions of life. The health workers have always said that the main struggle for health takes place outside the health centre, and they believe they have a role in serving and helping to build this activity. But with the pressure of work, this theoretical commitment has sometimes got lost. Recently they have come under fire from local trade unions and tenants' associations: 'You lot think you are the centre of the universe. We are doing more for people's health than you ever will. Why don't you send anyone to our meetings any more?' So recently the health centre's workers have renewed their efforts, going out into community centres, factories and offices. They advise on existing research on pollution, damp and shiftwork.

They help people to do their own surveys. They feed back evidence from their own record-keeping and epidemiological work to the workplace and community organizations. Recognizing how much more could be learned about the effects of work and home life on health, they are encouraging groups to document their experience. The shiftwork group, involving shop stewards from a biscuit factory, a hospital and a recently unionized group of office cleaners, is looking at what has been written on shiftwork, discussing it in the light of members' experience and planning a local study.

The centre has other research projects on the go too. The herbalists, with some people from the pensioners' health group and the local oral history group, are collecting 'old wives' tales'. The idea began when the pensioners realized that they had remedies for minor illnesses which the practitioners had never heard of, from cures for cramp in bed to treatments for minor sprains. Another project is assessing the relevance of different kinds of healing, particularly to chronic illness, cancer and infectious diseases. The evaluation takes account not only of outcome, but of the effects of the different approaches on the experience of being ill. A third project is looking at digestive problems. It began when one of the women's groups realized how many women they knew with chronic bowel problems, indigestion, constipation and diarrhoea. By using herbs and changes in diet, the problems can be mitigated. But what is causing this epidemic of abnormal digestion? Is there a common pattern in the lives of women with chronic bowel problems? The group has pieced together some new ideas about the origins of these disorders and is writing them down.

'Democratizing knowledge' is another of the centre's slogans. Teaching and mutual education are seen as a key part of the centre's work. There are introductory health courses for men and women and a special health course for older people. These involve a mixture of basic knowledge of physiology and anatomy, some ideas about healing and time to talk about feelings and experiences. There is also a more extensive 'Introduction to healing' course. The practitioners run workshops introducing, for instance, massage, the use of herbs and self-help therapy. There are courses on health and safety at work, do-it-yourself epidemiology, diet and nutrition, and the history of medicine and healing. The centre has considered starting its own training school, teaching full-time practitioners of the new medicine. But this is beyond their resources and for the moment seems premature.

As back-up to the research and education projects, the centre has a resource centre. The resource worker has specialized in developing health education materials to replace the old unusable ones. The new materials concentrate on straightforward introductions to the workings of the body and information about live health issues. For instance, there has been information on food additives, lead and the dangers of common domestic chemicals. Sometimes the production of health education materials in itself leads to more learning and the development of ideas. Two drafts of leaflets on cancer have recently been abandoned. The first, which advised on the early warning signs of cancer, was thrown out by the patients' advisory group because it was said to give false hope of cure. A second on the ins and outs of cancer treatment was felt to be insensitive and frightening.

The resource centre is also proud of its hazards computer. The computer stores both up-to-date toxicological information and details of campaigns against particular hazards which have taken place all over the world. With it, the known hazards of many chemicals used in homes, offices, factories and other workplaces can be checked, and if necessary contact can be made with other groups and organizations who have sought to reduce the hazard.

The centre prepares for its evening session. Four receptionists are on duty. The pharmacy and herbalist is open, and six practitioners are seeing individual patients. Mutual support groups for people with epilepsy, asthma, compulsive eating and drinking problems will all be meeting this evening. There is also a support group for people addicted to tranquillizers, a fertility clinic, which provides advice on self-insemination, and a blood pressure clinic which uses bio-feedback and advice on diet and exercise as an alternative to blood pressure tablets. Half a dozen people come down the stairs armed with spray cans. They are the tobacco action group going out to deface cigarette advertisements. They want to develop a consciousness of the hazards of smoking based on anger with the tobacco industry rather than self-inflicted guilt.

But the main event this evening is the monthly meeting of the centre's co-ordinating committee. The committee, made up of delegates from each of the neighbourhood blocks plus representatives of the centre's staff, takes responsibility for running the centre, deciding how much money should be spent and arbitrating in disputes about the centre's work. Anyone can come and speak, but only the committee members have votes. Usually it is very crowded and the meetings are noisy and argumentative. In periods when the meetings have been quiet some delegates have worried that if people don't want to discuss the centre, it is becoming irrelevant to their needs. Tonight the meeting will discuss the next steps in the campaign against cuts in the centre's budget. The health authority has formally complained about the centre's practice of encouraging people to take a friend or go in a group to see hospital specialists. The committee will decide how to respond to these charges of disruption. The pensioners' health group want to talk about the drop in numbers at their meetings. They say it is because the bus pass has been abolished and pensioners are getting more and more frightened to leave their homes, even during the day. The group wants to know what steps the centre can take.

The main debate of the evening has been raised by the home care unit. The unit's staff nurse sick people at home and provide helpers for permanently disabled people. They would like to do more. They say their support for people coming out of hospital is skimpy. Others who could be looked after at home are having to go into hospital for want of home nurses. When the unit was established it was seen as supplementing hospital care, not replacing it. It was argued that endless money could go into schemes which would just prop up the hospital's inadequate care. The home care unit say they have not got the resources to implement a new approach. They have always specialized in the best possible care for the dying, for instance, but they cannot release enough people to do this. As the hospital service becomes less and less adequate the unit's workload has doubled, but its resources have not. When the centre was first set up one of its many sayings was 'Care, not cure'; yet recently more and more resources have gone into taking on more and more practitioners, instead of into caring jobs. The unit has accused the centre of standing by while the old subordination of nursing to medicine is reproduced, and of giving jobs to friends of the practitioners rather than to people in greater need of work. 'The centre is becoming more interested in developing its fancy theories than in looking after people. The "new medicine" is becoming more and more airy-fairy while dying people suffer for want of a bath or a hot meal', the unit claims.

We cannot stay for the committee meeting.[1] We have no answers, no words to put in the delegates' mouths. We must leave them to it and come back to thinking about here and now, the crisis in health care and what we would like to see. The point of fantasy is not to spell out a programme, or insist that this is how it should be, but to provide something to argue around. How might health care change? What hopes are there for oppositional practice? How can we build resistance? Can the pain be turned outwards?

Notes and References

Place of publication is London unless otherwise stated.

Acknowledgements

1. Lesley Doyal, *The Political Economy of Health* (Pluto, 1979).
2. Mick Carpenter, 'Left Orthodoxy and the Politics of Health', *Capital and Class* No. 11, Summer 1980.

Chapter 1: Who Gets Ill?

1. Friedrich Engels, *The Condition of the Working Class in England* (Progress Publishers, Moscow, 1973), p. 134.
2. Geoffrey Rose and M. G. Marmot, 'Social class and coronary heart disease', *British Heart Journal* 1981: 45: pp. 13–19.
3. ibid.
4. For a discussion of some of the weaknesses of official statistics on women's health, see Alison Macfarlane, 'Official Statistics and Women's Health and Illness' in *Women and Government Statistics*, Equal Opportunities Commission Research Bulletin No. 4, Autumn 1980.
5. *Occupational Mortality: Decennial Supplement 1970–1972* (Office of Population Censuses and Surveys Series DS No. 1, 1978).
6. Peter Townsend and Nick Davidson, *Inequalities in Health: The Black Report* (Penguin, 1982), p. 51.
7. *Occupational Mortality*, p. 190.
8. ibid.
9. A. J. Fox and P. O. Goldblatt, *Longitudinal Study* (OPCS, Series LS No. 1, 1982).
10. OPCS, *General Household Survey 1980* (HMSO, 1982).
11. The authors of the Whitehall study on heart disease among civil servants suggest that it shows a steeper mortality gradient because the

people studied are better classified into more homogeneous groups than in the national statistics, so there is less error to cloud the effects: op. cit., p. 17.

12. OPCS, *Morbidity Statistics from General Practice 1970–1971, Socio-economic analyses* (HMSO, 1982).

13. Adrian C. Davis, 'Hearing disorders in the population: First phase findings of the MRC National Study of Hearing' in M. E. Lutman and M. P. Haggard, *Hearing Science and Hearing Disorders* (Academic Press, 1983).

14. George Brown and Tirrill Harris, *Social Origins of Depression* (Tavistock, 1978).

15. Margaret Wynn and Arthur Wynn, *Prevention of Handicap and the Health of Women* (Routledge and Kegan Paul, 1979).

16. A. Macfarlane and J. Fox, 'Child Deaths from Accidents and Violence', *Population Trends* No. 12, Summer 1978.

17. A. Macfarlane, op. cit.

18. Ingrid Waldron, 'Employment and Women's Health: An analysis of causal relationships', *International Journal of Health Services* Vol. 10, No. 3, 1980, pp. 435–54.

19. There has been a long debate in epidemiology about why the mortality rates of married people, particularly married men, often appear to be lower. Some argue that marriage 'protects' against illness. Others believe the lower death rate simply reflects the possibility that ill people are less likely to marry. This 'protection or selection' debate is discussed briefly in the *Longitudinal Study*, p. 42.

20. M. Young, B. Bernard and G. Wallis, 'The mortality of widowers', *Lancet* Vol. ii, 1963, pp. 454–6.

21. Unpublished tables from the *Longitudinal Study*, with thanks to Kath Moser.

22. Townsend and Davidson, op. cit., p. 67.

23. Department of Health and Social Security, Social Security Statistics (HMSO, 1981).

24. *General Household Survey 1980* (HMSO, 1982), Table 7.1.

25. There are some illnesses, such as asthma, which appear to occur more often in better-off families. Researchers point out, however, that often the way a disease is defined is in itself a product of a class judgement by doctors. It may be, for instance, that doctors tend to give a diagnosis of 'asthma' in middle-class children and 'bronchitis' in

working-class children. Leukaemia is unusual among the cancers in not occuring more often among working-class people, but this may be because the diagnosis is masked by other conditions.

Chapter 2: Some Causes: Research and People Talking

1. Owen Lloyd and Clifford Peacock, 'Something in the air', *Times Health Supplement*, 26 February 1982.

2. See, for example, Royal College of Physicians, *Smoking and Health Now* (Pitman Medical, 1971).

3. Samuel S. Epstein and Joel B. Schwartz, 'Fallacies of lifestyle cancer theories', *Nature* v. 289, 15 January 1981, pp. 127–30.

4. Patrick Kinnersley, *The Hazards of Work and How to Fight Them* (Pluto, 1973). Offices can also be hazardous; see *The Office Workers' Survival Handbook* (British Society for Social Responsibility in Science, 1981).

5. Kinnersley, op. cit., p. 33.

6. D. M. Fanning, 'Families in flats', *British Medical Journal*, 1967, 4, pp. 382–6.

7. Caroline Bedale and Tony Fletcher, 'A damp site worse', *Times Health Supplement*, 12 February 1982.

8. Mary Brennan and Val Little, 'Housing and Health', *Medicine and Society* Vol. 5, 1979, pp. 8–11.

9. M. E. Brennan and R. Lancashire, 'Association of childhood mortality with housing status and unemployment', *Journal of Epidemiology and Community Health*, 1978, 32, pp. 28–33.

10. Campaign for Lead Free Air, *Evidence to the Royal Commission on Pollution* (CLEAR, 1982).

11. Lloyd and Peacock, op. cit.

12. Jennie Popay, 'Unemployment: A threat to public health' in *Unemployment: Who Pays the Price?*, Poverty Pamphlet No. 53 (Child Poverty Action Group, 1982).

13. Brennan and Lancashire, op. cit.

14. At a recent conference about women and health, a paper on women and unemployment suggested that when men become unemployed they experience for the first time what Betty Friedan, talking about the feelings of women isolated at home, called 'the problem which has no name'.

15. *Trouble with Tranquillisers* (Release Publications, 1982).

16. *Food and Profit* (Politics of Health Group, 1979).

17. Samuel Epstein, *The Politics of Cancer* (Anchor Books, New York, 1979), pp. 182–5.

18. Margaret Wynn and Arthur Wynn, *Prevention of Handicap and the Health of Women* (Routledge and Kegan Paul, 1979).

19. *Household Food Consumption and Expenditure 1980*, Annual Report of the National Food Survey Committee (HMSO, 1982), Table 20.

20. OPCS, *General Household Survey 1980* (HMSO, 1982).

21. Joseph Eyer and Peter Sterling, 'Stress-Related Mortality and Social Organisation', *Review of Radical Political Economics* Vol. 9, No. 1, Spring 1977.

22. Kinnersley, op. cit., p. 20.

23. R. Sibert, 'Stress in Families of Children who have Ingested Poisons', *British Medical Journal*, 12 July 1975, pp. 87–9.

24. 'The child's hazards in utero' in J. G. Howells (ed.), *Modern Perspectives in International Child Psychiatry* (Brunner/Hazel, New York, 1971).

25. For an account of the hazards of BisCME see Samuel Epstein, op. cit. (note 17).

Chapter 3: Conditions of our Lives

1. *Inequalities in Health: The Black Report* (republished by Penguin Books, 1982), written by a working group chaired by Sir Douglas Black, president of the Royal College of Physicians, is a major source of information on class differences in health. Originally commissioned by the Labour government, the report proved an embarrassment to the Conservative government.

2. A summary of these arguments on what makes us ill can be found in Lesley Doyal, *The Political Economy of Health* (Pluto, 1979), Chapter 2, 'Health and Illness and the Development of Capitalism in Britain'. Two pamphlets present a similar case: *What are the REAL causes of illness? How can we be healthy?* (Socialist Health Association) and *It's My Life, Doctor* (Brent Community Health Council).

3. In recent years radical epidemiologists have argued that most epidemiology is 'positivist' and geared to the possibilities of minor

reforms, not criticism of social structures. Its methods of study reduce our experience to small compartments amenable to study by statistical methods and are inappropriate to the critique of whole social structures. The search for a materialist rather than a positivist epidemiology is the perspective which underlies this chapter. For a critique of positivist epidemiology see, for instance, Keith Paterson, 'Theoretical Perspectives in Epidemiology – A Critical Appraisal', *Radical Community Medicine*, Autumn 1981. In the United States in the late 1970s a group of Marxist health workers produced a series of papers in search of a historical materialist epidemiology; see *The Social Etiology of Disease* Part One: HMO Packet No. 2, Part Two: HMO Packet No. 3, published by the Network for Marxist Studies in Health. Unfortunately these papers are difficult to obtain in Britain. The same perspective can be found in some papers in the *Review of Radical Political Economics* Vol. 9, No. 1, Spring 1977.

4. Think, for instance, of the men in the Whitehall study. They shared the same environment, and none of them probably was subject to significantly different environmental hazards; but their health was very different.

5. We are so familiar with the notion of 'germs' that it comes as a shock that in the nineteenth century 'germ theory' was hotly contested. Surprisingly even Florence Nightingale was an anti-contagionist. George Bernard Shaw was another fierce opponent of germ theory: see, for instance, his *The Doctor's Dilemma: A Tragedy* (Constable, 1911) and the 'Preface on Doctors' which goes with it. For the history of the germ theory controversy, see E. H. Ackerneckt, *A Short History of Medicine* (Ronald Press, New York, 1968).

6. R. J. Meyer and P. J. Haggerty, 'Streptococcal Infections in Families', *Pediatrics* 29, 1962, pp. 532–49.

7. S. J. Schleifer, 'Bereavement and Lymphocyte Function', Presentation to the American Psychiatric Association Annual Meeting, San Francisco, May 1980, quoted in Larry Dossey, *Space, Time and Medicine* (Shambhala, Colorado, 1982).

8. George Vaillant, 'Natural History of Male Psychologic Health', *New England Journal of Medicine*, 6 December 1979, pp. 1249–54. The letters which followed the publication of this article (3 April 1980, p. 816) are as fascinating as the article itself. One correspondent comments: 'For six years I have been involved in research on the prevention of heart

disease. To me the most impressive observation of this study has been the high level of misery among the middle-aged male participants'.

9. The view I give here is very crude. It argues only that our emotional lives can bear on our health and does not explore what the nature of that relationship might be. This is the crucial issue at the core of therapeutic practice. Reichian therapists would argue, for instance, that feeling in itself can never make us ill. Illness occurs because of blocked feelings. From this point of view, what we need for our health has not just to do with changing our lives but with the release of blocked feelings. Once this happens, how we want our lives to change will become clearer. In some ways it seems like a political slidy slope to say that the problem for our health is not the conditions of our lives, but our blocked feelings about them. It may be, however, that in the release of those feelings we see more clearly what it is we don't like and want to change. It may also be that in so doing we discover the nature of our own power.

10. Time is a key concept in Marxist theory, which analyses exploitation in terms of the concept of labour time and alienation. Exploitation is measured by subtracting the hours you would have to work to produce goods equivalent to what you are paid from the hours you actually work. Larry Dossey argues that it is the construction of time in modern industrial societies which is destroying our health (op. cit.).

11. *Longitudinal Study* (OPCS Series LS No. 1, 1982).

12. Health is amoral. Some alternative views of healing – particularly Eastern views – equate health with virtue. The good health of the ruling class, however, reminds us that health like wealth can be obtained at other people's expense. Health is often seen as reflecting a spiritual condition. It is perhaps salutary to consider that it is possible to be healthy while being cynical and exploitative, not only of the people you make money out of but of emotional servicers, including wives and secretaries. There are other conundrums this book does not have space to explore. Most importantly, why do women live longer than men? Crudely we might imagine their greater oppression would lead to shorter lives. There are various theories. Women may be biologically stronger (more girls than boys survive even at birth). They take fewer risks and have fewer accidents. They may hang on to life more. Looking after children may be isolating, but finally it may be much less alienating than working in a factory. Survival may be more important to women

than men. We can only speculate; it is an area which it would be interesting to explore further.

Chapter 4: Common Treatment

1. Throughout writing this book I had enormous support, advice and help from Gene Feder, who, while a doctor himself, has helped me to clarify the criticisms of medicine I have presented. The inclusion of my sister's experiences in the book, however, has caused more sustained and heated arguments between us than any other aspect of our work. Gene insists that young asthmatics can die suddenly and that the procedures adopted to deal with Caroline's asthma attack were probably fully justified, on the principle of better safe than sorry.

Chapter 5: What Can Medicine Do?

1. Department of Health and Social Security, *Health and Personal Social Services Statistics 1982*, Table 4.4, p. 62.

2. *Compendium of Health Statistics* (Office of Health Economics, 1981), Table 1.1.

3. *The Pharmaceutical Industry and the Nation's Health* (Association of the British Pharmaceutical Industry, June 1982).

4. *Health Care Research Expenditure*, Office of Health Economics Briefing No. 6, June 1978.

5. Nicolas Wells, *Medicines: 50 Years of Progress 1930–1980* (Office of Health Economics).

6. OPCS, *Cancer Incidence, Survival and Mortality Rates* (OPCS Series SMPS No. 43, HMSO, 1981).

7. OPCS, *Cancer Statistics – Survival 1971–75* (OPCS Series MB No. 1, HMSO, 1982).

8. Dick Richards, *The Topic of Cancer* (Pergamon, 1982).

9. Mark McCarthy, *Epidemiology and Policies for Health Planning* (King Edward's Hospital Fund for London, 1982).

10. A. Colling, P. Carson and J. Hampton, 'Home or hospital care for coronary thrombosis', *British Medical Journal*, 13 May 1978, pp. 1254–9.

11. J. R. Hampton and C. Nicolas, 'Randomised trial of a mobile

coronary care unit for emergency calls', *British Medical Journal*, 29 April 1978, pp. 1118–21.

12. 'New Hope for Heart Programme', *Doctor* Vol. 12, No. 34, 26 August 1982, p. 32.

13. In the United States well over 500 operations are carried out per million population, while English research has estimated that fewer than 50 patients per million need the operation. Source: McCarthy, op. cit., p. 29.

14. W. A. Check, 'Have pacemakers found their way into too many patients?' *Journal of the American Medical Association* Vol. 243, No. 23, 20 June 1980, pp. 2371–2.

15. Donald J. Lane and Anthony Storr, *Asthma: the Facts* (OUP, 1979), p. 117.

16. *British National Formulary No. 4* (British Medical Association and the Pharmaceutical Society of Great Britain, 1982), p. 44.

17. Martin Weitz, *Health Shock* (Hamlyn Paperbacks, 1982).

18. 'Choosing a Non-Steroid Anti-Inflammatory Drug', *Drug and Therapeutics Bulletin* Vol. 19, No. 14, 3 July 1981.

19. *British National Formulary No. 4* (op. cit.).

20. The terminology for mental illness used here, 'anxiety', 'depression', 'schizophrenia' and 'psychosis', follows medical terminology. This does not, however, imply an acceptance of medicine's conceptual framework. In Chapter 8 we discuss the limitations of medicine's diagnostic categories for physical illnesses. In the same way medicine's categories for mental illness should be seen as no more than *one* possible naming system.

21. R. D. Laing, *The Politics of Experience and the Bird of Paradise* (Penguin, 1967).

22. *Trouble with Tranquillisers* (Release Publications, 1982), p. 17.

23. M. P. Vessey *et al.*, 'Dilation and curettage in young women', *Health Bulletin* Vol. 37, No. 2, March 1979, pp. 59–62.

24. *In Defence of the NHS* (Radical Statistics Group of the British Society for Social Responsibility in Science, 1979).

25. Alison Macfarlane, 'Studies of cerebral palsy' in I. Chalmers and G. McIlwaine (ed.), *Perinatal audit and surveillance* (Royal College of Obstetricians and Gynaecologists, 1981).

26. US Department of Health Education and Welfare, 'Report of the First Task Force on predictors of intrapartum fetal distress' in *Ante-*

natal diagnosis, Publication No. 79 (Washington National Institute of Health, 1979)'

27. Iain Chalmers *et al.*, 'Obstetric practice and outcome of pregnancy in Cardiff', *British Medical Journal*, 27 March 1976, pp. 735–8.

28. A. M. Flynn, J. Kelly, G. Hollins and P. P. Lynch, 'Ambulation in labour', *British Medical Journal*, 1978, 2, pp. 581–93.

29. F. J. Huygen, 'Home deliveries in Holland', *Journal of the Royal College of GPs* Vol. 26, No. 165, April 1976, pp. 244–8.

30. Thomas McKeown, *The Role of Medicine* (Blackwell, 1979), pp. 91–113.

31. *Martindale's Extra Pharmacopoeia* (Pharmaceutical Society).

32. OPCS, *Communicable disease statistics 1980* (OPCS Series MB2 No. 7, HMSO, 1982), Table 16.

33. C. Barr Taylor and Stephen Fortmann, 'Essential Hypertension', *Psychosomatics* Vol. 24, No. 5, May 1983.

34. Editorial, 'Millions of mild hypertensives', *British Medical Journal*, 18 October 1980, pp. 1024–5.

35. Jill Rakusen, 'Feminism, and the Politics of Health', *Medicine in Society* Vol. 8, No. 1, 1982.

36. Lisa Saffron, 'Cervical cancer: the politics of prevention', *Spare Rib* No. 129, April 1983.

37. A. Sheiham, 'Is there a scientific basis for six-monthly dental examinations?', *Lancet* ii: 442–4, 1977.

38. A. Sheiham, 'Sugars and dental decay', *Lancet* i: 282–4, 1983.

39. P. C. Gray, J. E. Todd, G. L. Slack and J. S. Bulman, *Adult Dental Health in England and Wales in 1968* (HMSO, 1970).

40. ibid.

41. Sheiham, 1977, op. cit.

42. R. J. Elderton, 'The causes of failure of restorations: a literature review', *Journal of Dentistry* 4: 257–62, 1976.

43. R. J. Elderton in H. Allred (ed.), *Assessment of the Quality of Dental Care* (London Hospital Medical College, 1977), p. 80.

44. McKeown, op. cit.

Chapter 6: The Subjugation of Care

1. For a discussion of the way hospitals, and particularly nurses, are portrayed in television and fiction, see Jane Salvage, 'Angles not Angels', *The Health Services*, 3 September 1982.

2. DHSS, *Health and Personal Social Services Statistics 1982*, Table 4.5, p. 66.

3. McKeown, *The Role of Medicine* (Blackwell, 1979).

4. Jeannette Mitchell, 'Health workers becoming even stronger', *Spare Rib* No. 124, October 1982, p. 25.

5. The guidelines for the new management structures in the NHS, introduced on the advice of McKinsey, are set out in what has come to be known as the Grey Book. Its formal title is DHSS, *Management Arrangements for the Reorganised National Health Service* (HMSO, 1972). McKinsey and Co. also influenced the new management structures in local government around the same time; see Cynthia Cockburn, *The Local State* (Pluto, 1977).

6. 'NHS Management Inquiry', DHSS Press Release, 3 February 1983.

7. See Peter Parker, 'The nurses who said "No"', *The Health Services*, 15 October 1982, and Virginia Beardshaw, *Conscientious Objectors at Work* (Social Audit, 1981).

8. Pressure to reduce the length of hospital stay came directly from the Treasury in the mid-1970s. See HM Treasury, *Saving Hospital Expenditure by Reducing In-Patient Stay* (Government Economic Service Occasional Papers No. 14, HMSO, 1977). This paper explicitly states that it is the early discharge of acute patients that gives the greatest possibilities for economy.

9. A joint letter from the Administrator and the Chairman of the Medical Council of St Bartholomew's Hospital to all consultants, senior registrars and registrars on 14 January 1983 is typical: it begins 'Due to the current severe flu epidemic, this hospital has become seriously congested, to the point where it has been impossible to find beds either for routine or emergency admission'.

10. 'There is a tradition of post-operative "rehabilitation" after hysterectomy, which is without clear benefit': Mark McCarthy, *Epidemiology and Policies for Health Planning* (King Edward's Hospital Fund for London, 1982), p. 137.

11. See J. S. A. Ashley, D. J. Lawrence and J. Hughes, *The Inappropriate Use of Hospital Beds: A survey of local investigations into the 'blocked bed' problem* (Department of Community Health, London School of Hygiene and Tropical Medicine, 1981).

12. 'Norman Fowler on the Future of Tadworth Court', DHSS Press Release, 14 March 1983.

13. The proper name of the Department of Health is of course the Department of Health and Social Security. Throughout the subsequent chapters this shortened form is also used.

14. DHSS, *Health Service Costing Returns*, year ended 31 March 1982, pp. 36–7.

15. DHSS, *Health and Personal Social Services Statistics 1982*, Table 2.5, p. 18.

16. For a powerful account of the way medicine both defines and abandons mentally handicapped people, see Joanna Ryan with Frank Thomas, *The Politics of Mental Handicap* (Penguin, 1980).

Chapter 7: Intimate Encounters

1. There are at least four magazines regularly sent free to GPs: *Pulse*, *Doctor*, *General Practitioner* and *Medeconomics*. Each is self-financing through drug advertising. All carry articles on financial management in general practice and how to maximize on the fees available from the DHSS. *Medeconomics* is solely devoted to doctors and money.

2. John Berger's book *A Fortunate Man* (Writers and Readers, 1976) portrays such a doctor.

3. Black people come particularly high on the list of non-compliers.

4. Cherrill Hicks, 'The price of a prescription', *Nursing Times* Vol. 80, No. 1, 16 March 1983, pp. 9–11.

5. Source: *The Pharmaceutical Industry and the Nation's Health* (Association of the British Pharmaceutical Industry, June 1982).

6. For a longer account of racism in the health service, see *Black People and the Health Service* (Brent Community Health Council, 1981).

7. ibid.

8. The TB rate among the native population in Britain is declining; see 'Memorandum for the Joint Tuberculosis Committee', *British Medical Journal*, 22 April 1978.

9. Very few people actually arrive with active TB, but after three

months there is a steady increase in the number of people with it, and it is thought that a change of resistance to TB may occur within a few months of people coming into Britain. See R. Grenville-Mathers and J. B. Clark, 'The development of tuberculosis in Afro-Asian immigrants', *Tubercle* 60, 1979, pp. 25–9, and P. Cole's paper for a symposium at Northwick Park Hospital, 1976.

10. *The Medical Examination of Immigrants* (British Medical Association pamphlet, 1966).

11. *Black People and the Health Service* (op. cit.).

12. *Keeping Warm in Winter* (Health Education Council). Research indicates that pensioners are sometimes not aware that they are cold. This is, however, all the more reason why they should have sufficient heating.

> *Hypothermia*
> Not because the neighbours never know
> Not because too tired to light a fire
> The old who seem to die of cold do not
> They die for want of coins for the slot

From Audrey Beechâm, *Different Weather* (Weybrook Press, 1980).

13. DHSS, *Prevention and Health: Eating for Health* (HMSO, 1978).

14. DHSS, *Prevention and Health: Avoiding Heart Attacks* (HMSO, 1981).

15. DHSS, *Prevention and Health: Reducing the Risk. Safer Pregnancy and Childbirth* (HMSO, 1977).

16. A letter from the Hull District Community Physician to local GPs written in October 1979 spells this out: 'As it is impossible to fit a quart into a pint pot, it is obvious that the number of priorities granted on medical grounds must be severely limited ...' In this letter the DCP effectively tells doctors that a certificate of need for rehousing will be ignored unless accompanied by a special personal plea directly to himself from the GP: 'It is obvious from reading between the lines on these medical certificates that many of them are written by the doctor himself simply to placate the patient. I accept these placatory certificates as a fact of life and the practice will continue. However, if any doctor feels very strongly that a case should be brought to my notice, then in those very few cases he should contact me in person.'

17. Jane Feinman, 'Outside I can't control the environment', *General Practitioner*, 17 February 1983.

18. For a more general look at the way state agencies reproduce the relations of production, see the London Edinburgh Weekend Return Group, *In and Against the State* (Pluto, 1980).

Chapter 8: Inside Medicine

1. G. B. Shaw, 'Preface on Doctors' in *The Doctor's Dilemma: A Tragedy* (Constable, 1911), p. xxxiii.

2. The battle against disease is powerfully described by Brian Hurwitz, quoted in Karl Filio's 'Sinister Medicine?', *Radical Science Journal* No. 9, p. 17. Brian Hurwitz comments: 'Without actually being aware of it, the patient arrives and in a sense finds himself or herself in the middle of a war – really a sort of frantic battle. And in some sense, this battle is going on independently of the patient. The struggle is really between doctors and disease: the patient is a sort of a vehicle for the fact that disease exists.'

3. S. Vaisrub, 'Groping for Causation', *Journal of the American Medical Association* 241: 8, 830, 1979.

4. Larry Dossey, *Space, Time and Medicine* (Shambhala, Colorado, 1982).

5. For a discussion of the way medical technology has developed, taking the search for explanation away from subjective experience, see Stanley Joel Reiser, *Medicine and the Reign of Technology* (Cambridge University Press, 1978).

6. See W. F. Brynum, E. J. Browne and Roy Porter, *Dictionary of the History of Science* (Macmillan, 1981), p. 100: 'Most of the diagnostic innovations of the 20th century have been sophisticated technical applications of 19th century concepts rather than the result of a wholly new intellectual orientation to disease. In this sense computed tomography (CAT or CT scanning) is in a direct line of descent from Paris Medicine and the arrythmia monitor is in the tradition of the kymograph.'

7. 'Disease *n.* a disorder with a specific cause and recognizable signs and symptoms; any body abnormality or failure to function properly except that resulting from physical injury (the latter may however open the way for disease)': *Concise Medical Dictionary* (Oxford University Press, 1980).

8. Thomas McKeown, *The Role of Medicine* (Blackwell, 1979), p. xii.

9. It is remarkable how blind we can be to the weakness of our own language and culture while criticizing others. Dr Philip Rack, a well-known expert on 'the health problems of immigrants', attributes the 'unrelated, bizarre and disproportionate' accounts of symptoms by Indian, Pakistani and Bangladeshi men to a weakness in their language. Asian culture describes unhappiness in bodily terms, he claims, because Asian people will not acknowledge they are miserable. It evidently does not occur to Dr Rack, whose job involves promoting a better under-standing of Asian culture in the NHS, that it may be our rather than their culture which is at fault. Our culture is impoverished by not having a tradition which reflects on the bodily experience of emotional states, often a better guide than the head language in which Dr Rack is confident of European superiority: Philip Rack, 'Unhappiness can make immigrants' life hell', *General Practitioner*, 11 December 1981, p. 57.

Chapter 9: Crisis and Restructuring

1. The government's health care policies during this period are set out in *Priorities for Health and Social Services in England* (HMSO, 1976) and *The Way Forward* (HMSO, 1977).

2. The RAWP policy is set out in *Sharing Resources for Health in England* (HMSO, 1976).

3. For a more detailed account of the way these policies affected London's health care services, see *Chronic and Critical: The Long Crisis in London's Everyday Health Care* (Community Health Councils in London, 1980).

4. *Compendium of Health Statistics* (Office of Health Economics, 1981), Table 1.9.

5. See John Yudkin, 'Changing patterns of resource allocation in a London teaching district', *British Medical Journal*, 28 October 1978, pp. 1212–14.

6. DHSS, *Health and Personal Social Services Statistics 1982*, Table 4.5, p. 66.

7. *Compendium of Health Statistics* (Office of Health Economics, 1981), Table 1.3.

8. The Department of Health's own study *Community Care* (DHSS,

1981) points out that adequate community care may not be cheaper. It also stresses that community care is dependent on women carers.

9. *Going Private. The case against private medicine* (Politics of Health Group and Fightback, 1982).

10. Gareth Griffiths, 'Private health care', *Financial Times*, 12 January 1983, pp. 13–14.

11. *First Report from the Expenditure Committee Session 1976/77, Preventive Medicine, Volume 1* (HMSO, 1977).

12. DHSS, *Prevention and Health: Everybody's Business* (HMSO, 1976).

13. White Paper *Prevention and Health* (HMSO, 1977).

14. DHSS, *Care in Action: A handbook of policies and priorities for the health and social services* (HMSO, 1981).

15. Jeannette Mitchell, 'Looking after ourselves', *Journal of the Royal Society of Health* No. 4, 1982, pp. 169–73.

16. 'Pharmacists are under-used for health care advice: Clarke', DHSS Press Release, 28 March 1983.

Chapter 11: Health Is Struggle

1. Nor would we necessarily want to abolish illness. Many alternative practitioners see overt acute illness as a healing crisis – literally a way of getting things out of our system.

2. Prescriptions for widespread social change as a response to illness are not new. Virchow, the famous nineteenth-century pathologist, prescribed as follows for the typhus epidemic in Upper Silesia in 1848: full democracy, education, liberty, prosperity, national autonomy, communal self-government, new roads, improvements in agriculture and industry, and co-operatives. See E. H. Ackerneckt, *Rudolf Virchow, doctor, statesman, anthropologist* (University of Wisconsin, Madison, 1953).

Chapter 12: Appropriate Health Care

1. *Compendium of Health Statistics* (Office of Health Economics, 1979), Figures 1.5, 1.6, 1.7, and *Compendium of Health Statistics* (OHE, 1981), Table 1.2.

2. *In Defence of the NHS* (Radical Statistics Group of the British Society for Social Responsibility in Science, 1979).

3. London Edinburgh Weekend Return Group, *In and Against the State* (Pluto, 1980).

4. Marshall Marinker, 'Should general practice be represented in the university medical school?', *British Medical Journal*, 12 March 1983, pp. 855–9.

5. For a discussion of the need for a new public health consciousness, see Peter Draper *et al.*, 'Health and Wealth', *Royal Society of Health Journal*, June 1977.

6. The Work Hazards Group which grew out of the British Society for Social Responsibility in Science was developed with the intention of making scientists' skills available to the labour movement. See *Hazards Bulletin*, the magazine of the group.

7. In 1976, for instance, a doctor from the Battersea People's Aid and Action Centre helped all the tenants of Sporle Court, a council-owned block, to submit a case on behalf of seventeen families for rehousing. See 'Sporle Court – An Everyday Story of Housing Mismanagement' in the *Evidence to the Morgan Crucible Enquiry* from Caroline Langridge, Secretary to Wandsworth Community Health Council.

8. Barbara Ehrenreich and Deirdre English, *For Her Own Good: 150 Years of the Experts' Advice to Women* (Pluto, 1979), p. 40.

9. For a historical perspective on the popular healing tradition, see Barbara Griggs, *Green Pharmacy: A history of herbal medicine* (Jill Norman and Hobhouse, 1982), and Ehrenreich and English, op. cit.

10. For a perspective which links present-day healing practice and psychotherapy with their roots in ancient traditions, see Richard Grossinger, *Planet Medicine* (Shambhala, Colorado, 1982).

11. Ehrenreich and English, op. cit.

12. S. S. Davis and M. Aslam, *The Hakim and His Role in the Immigrant Community*, Final Report to the DHSS, mimeo.

13. 'Your friendly neighbourhood Hakim', *World Medicine*, 26 July 1980.

14. 'Risk from Asian "healers"', *Hospital Doctor* Vol. 2, No. 6, 21 March 1979, p. 3.

15. Ehrenreich and English, op. cit.

16. ibid., pp. 42–52.

17. Griggs, op. cit., p. 202.

18. Although there is no legitimized language for this realm of experience in Western culture, such languages do exist. Chinese and Indian healing systems assume a unity of mind and body and have highly developed descriptive concepts.

19. Quoted in *It's My Life, Doctor* (Brent Community Health Council, 1982).

Chapter 13: Agenda

1. P. Pritchard, 'Patient Participation in Primary Health Care', *Health Trends* Vol. 11, 1979, pp. 92–5.

2. Barbara Ehrenreich and Deirdre English, *For Her Own Good: 150 Years of the Experts' Advice to Women* (Pluto, 1979).

3. Carlos E. Biro, 'In order to abolish primary health care workers', HMO packet No. 4, *Medicine and Ideology*, 1978 (mimeo, then available from Health Pac, 17 Murray Street, New York).

4. Dolores Burns (ed.), *The Greatest Health Discovery: Natural Hygiene and its Evolutions Past, Present and Future* (Natural Hygiene Press, Chicago, 1972), p. 137.

5. Gail Young, 'A woman in medicine: reflections from the inside' in Helen Roberts (ed.), *Women, Health and Reproduction* (Routledge and Kegan Paul, 1981), pp. 160–61.

6. See Robin Jenkins, *The Production of Knowledge at the Institute of Race Relations* (ILP Publications, 1971). This pamphlet argues that research is either about the people at the bottom for the people at the top or about the people at the top for the people at the bottom.

7. 'Stress on the buses', *Hazards Bulletin* No. 26, June 1981, p. 3.

8. *Campaigning Against Dampness*, Paper No. 7 (Services to Community Action and Tenants leaflet).

9. For a more comprehensive set of proposals for action on the drug companies, see the Haslemere Group, *Who Needs the Drug Companies* (War on Want), pp. 33–8.

10. ibid., p. 13.

11. ibid., p. 36.

Chapter 14: Wishful Thinking

1. The trouble with this chapter is that all the meetings involved sound incredibly tiring. If we are to take care of our health, we must find a form of socialist feminist practice which does not mean spending our lives permanently in meetings.

MORE ABOUT PENGUINS, PELICANS AND PUFFINS

For further information about books available from Penguins please write to Dept EP, Penguin Books Ltd, Harmondsworth, Middlesex UB7 0DA.

In the U.S.A.: For a complete list of books available from Penguins in the United States write to Dept DG, Penguin Books, 299 Murray Hill Parkway, East Rutherford, New Jersey 07073.

In Canada: For a complete list of books available from Penguins in Canada write to the Marketing Department, Penguin Books Australia Ltd, P.O. Box 257, Ringwood, Victoria 3134.

In New Zealand: For a complete list of books available from Penguins in New Zealand write to the Marketing Department, Penguin Books (N.Z.) Ltd, P.O. Box 4019, Auckland 10.

In India: For a complete list of books available from Penguins in India write to Penguin Overseas Ltd, 706 Eros Apartments, 56 Nehru Place, New Delhi 110019.

Published by Pelicans

INEQUALITIES IN HEALTH

THE BLACK REPORT

Edited by Peter Townsend and Nick Davies

'The most important single document on health since the war'
– *Labour Weekly*

In 1980 the government published a report called *Inequalities in Health* which has been acclaimed as one of the most significant pieces of research into the nation's health since the Beveridge Report in 1942. The report, however, did not find favour with the government and was not widely distributed.

In this Pelican Peter Townsend (author of *Poverty in the United Kingdom*) and Nick Davidson introduce the report and assess the enormous amount of material on such topics as regional, class and sex inequalities in health care. In addition they draw comparisons between the changing trends in health care throughout the world and point out the report's implications for the future.

What is to be done about . . . ?

These short and simple books, published in connection with the Socialist Society, will deal with the central social and political issues of the day. They will set out the arguments, provide information and answer important questions, offering a political agenda for the eighties.

WHAT IS TO BE DONE ABOUT THE FAMILY?
Lynne Segal

The protective nuclear family seems to be breaking down: the divorce rate is high, children are alienated from parents, the old are neglected. Here the authors explain and argue exactly *why* it is crucial for the future of society that the issues surrounding the family become subject to political analysis and action.

WHAT IS TO BE DONE ABOUT LAW AND ORDER?
J. Young and J. Lee

What is *meant* by law and order? Whose law and what order? This timely study examines all the issues, discussing the concept of a 'breakdown of society', the present threat to our liberty, and what is to be done about the increasingly confrontational nature of forces within society in the British Isles.

Other books in this series will discuss the environment, higher education, NATO, and violence against women.